WILLIAM HARVEY

ENGLISHMAN

Translated by Kenneth J. Franklin

William Harvey's *Exercitatio anatomica de motu cordis et sanguinis in animalibus*, 1628, newly done into English by Kenneth J. Franklin, and published at Oxford for the Royal College of Physicians by Blackwell Scientific Publications, 1957.

William Harvey as an old man: from a rare etching by
Richard Gaywood

KENNETH J. FRANKLIN

D.M., D.SC., F.R.C.P., F.R.S.

Emeritus Professor of Physiology in the University of London
Emeritus Fellow of Oriel College, Oxford
Hon. Member of the Harveian Society of London

———

WILLIAM HARVEY

ENGLISHMAN

1578–1657

MCMLXI

MACGIBBON & KEE

LONDON

FIRST PUBLISHED BY MACGIBBON & KEE 1961
© KENNETH J. FRANKLIN
PRINTED IN GREAT BRITAIN BY
EBENEZER BAYLIS & SON LTD.
WORCESTER & LONDON

Gratias agimus

IT IS a pleasant culmination to one's career as a 'circulator' to write a biography of William Harvey, the discoverer of the movement of the heart and blood in animals; and my very warm thanks are due to R. G. Davis-Poynter, Esq., for undertaking the publication of it, as well as to Sir Geoffrey Keynes for allowing me to rescind a gentlemen's agreement of some years' standing. For he most generously wrote, 'Of course you must go on and publish your book! It will be years before mine is done.'

In 1937, under the auspices of Charles C. Thomas, I published *A Monograph on Veins*, and used as a frontispiece for it a picture of Harvey, which now hangs in the study of Professor Robert Janker, of Bonn and Thomasberg, Germany, to whom this present book is dedicated. In 1933, under the auspices of the same publisher if immediately by the generosity of the Carnegie Corporation of New York via the History of Science Society, I studied, and translated, *De venarum ostiolis*, 1603, of Harvey's teacher at Padua, namely, Hieronymus Fabricius of Aquapendente (1533?–1619). But earlier, in 1927, I had published *Valves in Veins: an Historical Survey*, and much later, in 1952, *The History of Circulatory Research, leading to a wider view of the circulation*, and introducing into it word of recent work of the Nobel prizeman, Professor A. Hevesy.

I gratefully acknowledge the permission of Messrs Staples Press to quote as I wish from the third edition of my book, *A Short History of Physiology*, which can well be regarded as a background to this biography of William Harvey. The short history I am, with his agreement, dedicating to Dr George A. Cowan, with whom I was fortunate enough to co-operate in some dental research while I was still at

5

Bart's, and who is in addition one of the finest and kindliest colleagues any scientist could wish to have.

Also most gratefully acknowledged is the permission granted me by Messrs Blackwell Scientific Publications in respect of my own publications with them, and of the relevant essays contributed to *Circulation: a symposium*, 1938; this was also agreed by the Editor, Professor John McMichael, F.R.S. The Treasurer of the Royal College of Physicians, and Messrs Blackwell Scientific Publications together with him, are allowing me to reproduce the colour picture, made by the Wellcome Foundation Film Unit in 1937, of the Harvey portrait in oils which graces the Library of the College, dates from before the Great Fire of London, and has been attributed to Cornelius Janssen (Janson van Keulen), 1590–1644.

Messrs Macmillan and Co. Ltd. have very kindly let me use the account, given by the late Professor Herbert A. Evans in his book, *Highways and Byways in Oxford and the Cotswolds*, of King Charles I's famous night-ride of 3 June 1644, which went through Yarnton, the Oxfordshire village to which I retired. Ghostly sounds of the night-march are still, they say, heard in the village, but the present writer has nothing to add to the story from personal experience.

The attractive title-page from Jean Riolan, Jun.'s *Anthropographia et osteologia*, Paris, 1626, is reproduced by courtesy of Dr E. Ashworth Underwood and of the Wellcome Historical Medical Museum. Through the courtesy of the same kind people is reproduced a rare print of an etching of Harvey as an old man. This etching is that attributed to Richard Gaywood, was etched from the life, and is probably the last portrait of Harvey to be made during his lifetime; it was intended to serve as a frontispiece to his *Exercitationes anatomicae de generatione animalium*, 1651, and my figure derives from the impression in the Wellcome Historical Medical Museum.

6

The portrait of Caspar Hofmann (1572–1642) in 1632, i.e. at the age of 60, comes from Boissard's *Bibliotheca chalcographia*, 1650 edition and was kindly lent by Dr E. Ashworth Underwood.

I am much indebted to L. M. Payne, Esq., F.L.A., Librarian of the Royal College of Physicians, for leave to quote from his fascinating article on the Scarburgh Harveian Oration of 1662, and other publications. To J. L. Thornton, Esq., Librarian of St Bartholomew's Hospital Medical College, I am indebted for most continuous and welcome encouragement from that Institution. To yet a third Librarian, P.Wade, Esq., B.A., F.L.A., of the Royal Society of Medicine, I owe my introduction to Dr George Bates' 1685 book on the late Troubles in England, and also his sympathetic read-through of the typescript of the present book.

But among individuals I am most indebted to Miss Mary E. Morse, who up to the time of my retirement from Bart's was my very efficient Secretary there. It is she who has turned my worse-than Harveian handwriting into elegant typescript and thus has thereby made this book possible.

KENNETH J. FRANKLIN

Broomfield
Yarnton
Oxon.

FOREWORD

WILLIAM HARVEY resembles Napoleon in that his life is constantly being written and new material incorporated in each fresh effort to recall his greatness. The grandeur of his accomplishment in contrast with the feeble gropings and speculations of those who were supposed to have anticipated him has never been better demonstrated than in this book. Professor Franklin employs his new translation of the chapter on parturition from *De Generatione* which shows how clearly Harvey understood the placental circulation, anticipating almost completely the work of the Hunters a hundred years later. If Harvey had had a microscope—how far would he have gone? He had so little help beyond his own clear mind. This life shows him not to have been the theorizing, prescribing physician bound by the conventions of his time but an experimental physiologist, and comparative anatomist, a practising obstetrician and an operating surgeon.

A. DICKSON WRIGHT

INTRODUCTION
AND DEDICATION

IN THE First World War Robert Berthold Janker, who had been born in Munich on 12 March 1894, served on the west front in the German foot artillery just as I myself did in the British field artillery and trench mortars, and a comparison of times and places shows that we may well have shot at each other on more than one occasion, though fortunately without harm to either of us.

Then in 1933, when both of us were long past medical qualification, he most kindly offered, through my friend Mr E. H. Leach, who was then in Bonn, to make for me some cineradiographic film 'shots' in a field of physiology which at that time particularly attracted me. These 'shots' were so revealing and fascinating that in January 1934 I asked Dr Robert Janker if I could come to him to do some further research, and in that way we co-operated in our first joint venture.

I realized at once how greatly cincradiography could assist physiology, and I still recall very vividly watching the passage, through various cardio-vascular channels that were only about 50 cm. distant on the fluorescent screen from our eyes, of radiopaque material which we had injected. I remember thinking also that, with Robert Janker's technical aid, William Harvey could have conclusively demonstrated the circulation of the blood within a matter of minutes, and by means of the aeroplane could have distributed copies of the resultant film all round the world within a few days.

Since 1934, apart from the period of the Second World War, I have visited Professor Janker very often, and he has set a wonderful example throughout that time of selfless international co-operation in medicine, while contributing outstandingly to the technique, practice, and literature of both diagnostic and therapeutic radiology, and seeing with startling clarity into research problems and the means for their resolution; he has also devoted his time and his professional earnings without stint to advancing his speciality in all these different ways. His publications include nearly two hundred books and papers, but he has also produced a very large number of cineradiographic film records, some of them so beautiful as to be breathtaking when they are seen projected, and all technically first-class. He has also invented a consummate filing system for his half a million or more radiographs.

This tireless Bavarian, who for a long stretch of his life worked unremittingly for sixteen hours a day, is a superb and witty lecturer with a commanding voice, and is popular with his staff and students and colleagues and with the general public, in March 1959 entered into his sixty-sixth year. Learned Societies throughout the world paid tribute to him, and the Justus Liebig University of Giessen conferred on him an Honorary Doctorate, while His Excellency the President of the West German Republic presented him with das Grosse Bundesverdienstkreuz.

I ask this very great man and fine friend to accept dedication of this book. For, like Harvey, he can say, 'Sed solam veritatem sector; et omnem tum operam, tum oleum eo contuli, ut aliquid bonis gratum, doctis commodum, et rei literariae utile in medium proferre possim' (But without ceasing I follow truth only, and have devoted all my effort and time to being able to contribute something pleasing to good men and appropriate to learned ones, and of service to literature).

KENNETH J. FRANKLIN

ILLUSTRATIONS

As Dr Parkes says in his Harveian Oration, *1876*, 'When anyone examines into this discovery of Harvey's, and gradually recognizes its extraordinary importance, he cannot but be seized with an urgent wish to know how the mind which solved so great a problem was constituted; how it worked and how it reached, not merely the probability, but the certainty, of a grand natural law. . . . There was no accident about it—no help from what we call chance; it was worked out and thought out, point after point, until all was clear as sunshine in midsummer. Nor had it been anticipated.'

From G. T. Bettany, '*Eminent doctors: Their lives and their work*,' 1885, 1.

WILLIAM HARVEY

ENGLISHMAN

WILLIAM HARVEY

ENGLISHMAN

*

THE late Professor F. J. Cole, F.R.S., who was in charge of the Department of Zoology of Reading University from 1906 to 1939 (Eales, 1959; Franklin, 1960), wrote to me in 1937, 'When I am lecturing on the circulation I usually claim that the man who discovered it was he who established one-way traffic in the blood-vessels—out in the arteries and back in the veins. No oscillation in the vessels. I know of course that in the lower vertebrates Spallanzani and Haller did find some oscillation in the microscopic vessels but that was only exceptional. Now if you apply this test to the numerous claimants to the discovery, they all fail except Harvey himself, and the discovery of the circulation follows as a logical necessity of the one-way traffic in the vessels.' (Elsewhere (Cole, 1955) he drew a parallel with the discovery of one-way traffic in the nerves, the basis of the so-called Law of Forward Direction.)

If one judges by that criterion, one cannot say that Harvey derived at all from his predecessors in respect of the activity of the functioning cardiovascular system. As Payne (1896), however, wrote, 'While a long series of eminent men have so ably treated of the discovery of the circulation, and its consequences' in successive Harveian Orations, 'it would be difficult to add anything to what they have given us . . .' still I find that the genesis of Harvey's idea, and more especially its historical connexion with the labours of the great men of antiquity who laid the foundations of anatomy and physiology, have not received the same degree of attention.

Antecedents, however, not less than consequences, have to be taken into account in giving its true value to any scientific discovery. Certainly, Payne's own oration paid many well-deserved encomia to Galen, and I shall be content if before Galen I proceed to mention Alcmaeon, Aristotle, Herophilus, and Erasistratus, and after Galen various others.

Alcmaeon of Croton or Crotona, who flourished in the latter part of the sixth century B.C., thought that sleep was produced by the retreat of blood to the blood-carrying veins, and death by its total retreat to the same, while awakening was caused by its outpouring from them.

Some time after Alcmaeon came Aristotle (384–322 B.C.), the careful observer of animal life and one of the greatest of natural historians. His work is in consequence often referred to by Harvey, a score of times in *De motu cordis*, etc., and ten times that often in *De generatione animalium* (Fraser-Harris, 1924). Aristotle is of interest to our story in that he was a pioneer in natural history and embryology; he was also the first person to *illustrate* a biological treatise, though his drawings are lost. His chief object of embryological research was the developing chick, and it remains a popular one to this day, as it also was in *his* time to Harvey (*De generatione animalium*, etc.). Aristotle distinguished the classes of animals on anatomical, physiological, and embryological grounds, knew the important features of mammals, and anticipated conclusions of two millennia later than his own time by placing the *Cetacea* in or near these animals. He thought that the generation of most animals required the participation of two sexes, and that the egg was rendered capable of development by the sperm of the male. On the other hand, he believed in the spontaneous generation of some forms, an idea that was only finally refuted by Pasteur. He considered that a soul or psyche differentiated living from non-living substance, and that its activity resulted in form. Of this living principle he distinguished three types, the lowest concerned with nutrition and reproduction, the next with sensation, and the highest with intellect. Probably because he had found the brain experimentally unresponsive, he regarded the heart as the seat of intelligence, and the brain as an organ for its cooling by the secretion of pituita. With regard to the blood vessels, he said that as they 'advance, they become ever smaller, until at last their tubes are too fine to admit the blood'.

Anatomy was first placed on a definite footing by Herophilus of Chalcedon at Alexandria in the third century B.C. In physiology he regarded the brain as the central organ of the nervous system and the seat of intelligence, reversing thus the view held, as already noted, by Aristotle. He was the first to distinguish the nerves as concerned with movement and with sensation respectively. He differentiated arteries and veins, though in this he had been anticipated by Praxagoras of Cos about 335 B.C.; he was also the first to count the pulse and to make a detailed analysis of its variations; this he did with the aid of a clepsydra, or water-clock.

Erasistratus of Chios, somewhat the junior of Herophilus, was the second great figure of the Alexandrian school. He has been called 'the father of physiology', but others give that title to Galen, who went much further in animal experiment and who was not content, as was Erasistratus, to deny a function to certain organs, such as the spleen. For the most part, in any case, the work of Erasistratus has to be deduced from Galen's writings. He had a good knowledge of the anatomy of the heart and described the trachea, atria, cardiac valves and chordae tendineae. He is said to have differentiated the anterior and posterior spinal nerve roots respectively as motor and sensory in function. The diaphragm was, he thought, the only muscle concerned with respiration. Finally, he associated the higher intelligence of man with the greater elaboration of his cerebral convolutions. So far so good but, like all the ancients, he had to produce a general plan, largely theoretical, of the body's working. Erasistratus was a materialist and rationalist, and he accepted the atomium of the philosopher Democritus (c. 460–357 B.C.); he regarded nature as an external power acting upon the body.

The basis of his physiology, according to Singer, was his observation that every organ had a triple system of vessels: arteries, veins and hollow nerves. In these were found blood and two kinds of 'pneuma' (breath or spirit). These last were imaginary, and pneumatism can be traced back to the Hippocratic school; it was, however, to play an important part in retarding the development of physiology for centuries, so it is necessary to say more about it. Undoubtedly the idea at the back of the pneuma was in part an explanation, however imperfect, of the need of respiration for life, but it became elaborated to fill gaps in experimental knowledge of this and of other parts of physiology. A further point, which probably misled the ancients, e.g., Aristotle, was the fact that after violent death the liver, veins, and right heart are congested with blood, while the left heart and the arteries are relatively empty. The explanation which Erasistratus gave to account for this was that the blood is present in life in the liver, veins, and right heart alone, the arteries containing none. Air taken in by the lungs is changed in the left heart into a peculiar spirit, the spirit of life, and this is carried in the arteries to all parts of the body, including the brain. In the brain it is further changed into a second pneuma, the psychic spirit, which is further distributed to all parts by the hollow nerves. Erasistratus got over the fact that arteries bleed on being cut by saying that the escape of pneuma allowed a vacuum to form, and that blood flowed in from the veins through [hypothetical] anastomoses, which became patent only under such abnormal conditions.

Galen, the last of the ancients whom we shall consider, and whose writings were destined to dominate medicine for more than a thousand years, was born in Pergamum in

A.D. 130, when the Roman Empire was at the height of its power. At fifteen he commenced the study of philosophy and at eighteen that of medicine, and he combined both for the rest of his life. He travelled to Smyrna, Corinth, and Alexandria, where 'the science of physiology did not prosper. It was in bondage to the memory of the greatness of Erasistratus'. After four more years in Pergamum, he set out for Rome (A.D. 161) and soon established himself in the capital. It was not long before he was physician to the emperor, Marcus Aurelius, and his lectures were frequented by the leaders of society. He died about A.D. 200. The Harveian Oration for 1896, by F. J. Payne, is one of the best in the series, and is on the relation of Harvey to his predecessors and especially to Galen. It says on p. 12 that the relations of Harvey to Aristotle would be an interesting study.

Galen was a strange mixture. Though his name means 'Peaceful', he inherited a haughty and overbearing temperament. He had that feeling of intellectual superiority which was so common among the Greeks, though one must admit that in his case it had much justification. His chief fault, however, was that he believed himself acquainted with the 'final cause' of nature, the reason why things are as they are. By arrogating to himself such divine omnipotence he marred his true greatness. His belief was that God had made all the organs of the body as perfect as possible for their functions; he was not therefore so concerned with the 'efficient cause', i.e., how the parts of the body work.

The object of physiological research is to discover, by mainly experimental methods, how living beings carry out their various functions. If experiments are planned with care and skill, if fortune is with the physiologist, and if he interprets the results of his experiments without any bias, he will be able to make contributions of worth to his science. If, however, like Galen, he considers that he already knows the general scheme of nature, he will be much more liable to error, less enthusiastic, and less likely to advance his subject. Galen was an operator of consummate skill and ingenuity, but his experiments would have carried him to greater fame had he had no preconceived notions of nature's processes. He made many important discoveries which aided physiology, but he also left many ideas which retarded its development after him. Before analysing these, it is only right to note that he was the first to link up clinical observations with anatomy and physiology (and thereby to seek an explanation of pathological conditions in disorders of normal structure and function), and to say that he collected and synthesized all the medical knowledge of his predecessors. For those two things alone he would deserve our gratitude!

The advances which he made in physiological knowledge form an imposing list. In the physiology of the neuro-muscular system he showed, by experiments on primates and lower mammals, that longitudinal section causes complete loss of sensation and power of muscular movement below the level of the lesion. Semi-section causes muscular paralysis solely on the side of the lesion. He realized the segmented innervation of various muscles, and demonstrated the origin and functions of the phrenic nerve. He knew that the diaphragm was not the only muscle concerned in respiration and he showed the parts played respectively by it, the intercostals and the accessory muscles. He discovered the function of the recurrent laryngeal nerve, and at will stopped the cries of animals by tightening a ligature placed round this nerve. He said that sound was due to air vibrations, spoke of the antagonistic action of muscles and of muscle tone (*see* Sherrington, 1919), and differentiated voluntary from involuntary muscles. He believed in the intrinsic nature of the heart beat, and made important observations on the functions of the oesophagus, stomach, intestines and bladder. He knew of insensible perspiration. He observed the heart *in situ* with the thorax open but with both pleurae uninjured, and saw that both ventricles pulsate. Erroneously, he thought that cardiac and arterial diastoles were simultaneous. He disproved the view of Erasistratus that the left side of the heart and the arteries are empty of blood. In the case of the latter, he tied off a section of an artery and opened it to find it full of blood; obviously, there was no anastomosis of this portion with any vein. He proved this fact for various arteries, both deep and superficial. His other views on the functioning cardiovascular system will be considered after an analysis of his general idea of the body's working.

Galen postulated three pneumata where Erasistratus had had but two. The foodstuffs were taken as chyle from the alimentary canal to the liver, and there changed into blood. The lowest pneuma, the spirit of growth, was localized in the liver, veins and right heart, and with the flow and ebb of the venous blood was distributed to all parts of the body. In the lungs this blood was purified by the discharge of fuliginous vapours. The dynamic manifestation of this spirit of growth, the growth force, was concerned with sensual desires, nutrition and blood formation. It served thus for the nutrition and growth of the individual and of the species. The second pneuma, the spirit of life, was localized in the left heart and in the arteries; it was produced by the interaction of air (brought in from the lungs through what we now know as the pulmonary vein) with blood which passed from the right side of the heart to the left one through minute pores in the interventricular septum. The dynamic manifestation of this spirit of life, the pulsatile force, was concerned with courage, anger, personality and bodily heat. It served thus to ensure the activity of the heart, the production of heat in the left ventricle, and its distribution by the arteries; its auxiliary functions were connected with respiration and with the pulse. Some of this blood in the arteries reached the brain and in the ventricles of that organ was produced the third pneuma, or the spirit of the psyche. This spirit was localized in the brain and its dynamic manifestation, the psychic force, was concerned with intellectual activities, sensation, and movement. Intellectual activities were imagination, the power of thought, and memory. Sensation included vision, smell, taste, hearing and touch. Galen appears to have given the different functions differential localization in the brain, thus abolishing the 'sensorium commune' of Aristotle. The spirit of the psyche, finally, was only the chief agent of a soul (psyche) located in the brain substance, and served for the distribution throughout the body of the powers of sensitivity and movement.

The schema is a remarkable piece of constructive thought to account for the physiology of the whole body, but it was destined to do incredible harm to the progress of the science in question, because more stress was laid upon the schema than upon Galen's experimental work, and physiology cannot grow in an atmosphere of dogma, however ingenious that dogma may be.

The doctrine of the transmission of a very small amount of venous blood through invisible pores in the interventricular septum to the left side of the heart was Galen's logical deduction from the finding of blood in the arteries at a time when no communication was known to exist between what we now call the pulmonary artery and the pulmonary vein. Galen thought that the right atrio-ventricular opening was narrower than the aorta; this led him to postulate transference of some blood through the septum and this one assumption, unsupported by experimental proof, held up physiological progress for centuries. The present writer particularly regrets this as, according to Payne (1896, 30) Galen speaks also, more than once of the case of a boy in whom the chest walls were deficient from the results of an accident, so that the movements of the heart could be seen. Apparently, therefore, the case of Young Montgomery and his beating

26

heart (Harvey, 1651, 156–7) had been anticipated in Galen's clinical experience.

With that account, however imperfect, for lack of space, etc., we must leave the ancients. After Galen, for over a thousand years, physiology, in common with other intellectual activities, showed a retrogressive tendency. Rules for a concerted attack upon its problems were unformulated, and principles of criticism and research, which we can now draw from its historical study, were entirely absent. The idea of control experiments, as we now know it, had not yet been evolved. Neither of the two guiding principles in physiology, the integrative action of the circulatory system and the integrative action of the nervous system, was present to give order to the facts which had already been elucidated, and the circulation itself was unknown.

Between Galen's time and that of William Harvey (1578–1657) the most important contributions to the blood-movement story were:

(1) Views about alternative blood-pathways (i.e., pathways other than direct ones through the interventricular septum) from the right side of the heart to its left side. The first such view, now to be described, was that of Ibn an-Nafis. The later ones were those of Servetus (1553), Columbus (1559), Botallus (1564) and Caesalpinus (1571 and subsequently). For four of these five writers the alternative pathway was via what we now call the pulmonary artery and pulmonary vein; for the fifth, Botallus, it was from atrium to atrium via a persistent patent foramen ovale. None of the accounts described a blood circulation in our sense, even if we owe the actual word 'circulatio' to Caesalpinus.

(2) The views and physiological demonstrations of Leonardo da Vinci (1452–1519). These were not published at the time, and their main interest lies in the evidence which they provide of the waning deference to traditional views and of the revival of demonstrations in the living animal.

27

(3) The anatomies of Vesalius (1514–64) and of others, and the physiological demonstrations devised by Vesalius.

(4) The discovery of valves in veins.

These contributions were evidence of dissatisfaction with authority and of readiness to put forward new views and new facts, i.e., they were signs of healthy, if slow, progress in anatomy and physiology. On the other hand, the last two items far transcended the others in their ultimate importance to our story.

Knowledge of the contribution made by al-Qurashi, called Ibn an-Nafis (c. 1210–88), has only comparatively recently become available through the researches of an Egyptian physician, Muhyi ad-din at-Tatawi (1924), whose findings were confirmed and extended by Meyerhof, 1935. According to the latter, the most important events of the twelfth century A.D. were the foundation of the Nuri hospital in Damascus and the construction of the Nasiri hospital in Cairo. Ibn an-Nafis was a very learned doctor from Damascus, who was for a while in charge of the Nasiri hospital and also for some time Chief of the physicians in Egypt.

It was in his *Commentary on the Canons of Avicenna* that he produced his new ideas about the passage of blood from the right to the left side of the heart; briefly, they were as follows. The pores in the interventricular septum are closed ones and the cardiac substance there is thick. So there is no visible communication between the two heart chambers, as thought by some persons, or an invisible communication permitting the passage of blood, as alleged by Galen. Indeed, the septum is specially thick in order to prevent the direct passage of blood or spirit from ventricle to ventricle, for that might be harmful. What in fact happens is that blood is heated and refined in the right ventricle, and in consequence rises up in the artery-like vein [the pulmonary trunk

28

and its branches] to the lungs, where part of it is further refined by its transudation through the thick walls of the vein in question, the less refined part serving for the nutrition of the lungs themselves. The cleared and most refined fraction, plus considerable airy substance, passes back to the heart after penetrating through the thin walls of the vein-like artery [the pulmonary venous system] and in the left ventricle its further admixture with the air, brought with it from the lungs, gives it the necessary aptitude for the production of the spirit of life.

In addition to the above, Ibn an-Nafis stated that there are perceptible passages or pores between the artery-like vein and the vein-like artery; the pores in the artery-like vein are very close so that only very refined blood may transude from it. Finally, at the end of his considerations of the anatomy of the heart, he contended that the right ventricle has no active movement and that it is a matter of indifference whether one calls the heart a muscle or not.

Obviously, Ibn an-Nafis cannot be said to have discovered the pulmonary circulation; even if he did adumbrate in some measure its pathway, he allowed only a small portion of the right ventricular blood to make the circuit, and he made the right ventricle inactive. What he did do was to deny a direct interventricular communication; he had, therefore, to find an alternative pathway for a small amount of blood which had to be mixed with air in order that the spirit of life could be produced in the left ventricle. A very long time was to elapse before it became a practice of investigators to separate their observed facts from their hypotheses and ideas; indeed, quite a considerable time had to elapse before the former began to preponderate at all over the latter.

In the absence of any concept of a blood circulation in our modern sense, the main contribution of Ibn an-Nafis was, therefore, to emend an incorrect point in cardiac anatomy. It seems unlikely that his views exerted any marked influence, for there was no direct transmission of them to Servetus, who gave a somewhat similar account of the pulmonary blood pathway three centuries later; in addition, scepticism about an interventricular passage for the blood had similarly to appear, as if *de novo*, in the sixteenth century.

Leonardo da Vinci (1452–1519), the great Italian, had as his medical sources chiefly the Arabic derivatives of the classical writings, but he was not overawed by authority. The full significance of his drawings and notes was not appreciated until long after his day, and they had no marked influence on the progress of physiological thought, for they did not become common property.

He dissected, however, the bodies of men and of animals, and was the first after Aristotle to realize the scientific value of accurate illustration. The combination of artist and anatomist which he exhibited has, indeed, probably never been equalled. 'If the impulse to the new anatomy came from the artists, Leonardo may well be recognized as its originator and Vesalius as its great protagonist.' Da Vinci was a firm believer in observation and experiment and, whenever possible, preferred to explain a phenomenon as resulting from natural causes. He believed that no human findings could be termed true knowledge if they did not proceed to mathematical demonstration. He held teleological views not unlike those of Galen and stated that 'nothing is superfluous and nothing lacking in any kind of animal and product of nature'. His physiology was in many respects an advance on that of Galen, though it retained much that was galenic. As a result of his experiments on inflation of the lungs, he concluded that it was impossible for air as such to reach the heart; he considered that what we now know as the pulmonary arteries received the 'freshness of the air' from the bronchi. In regard to the blood vessels, he regarded the heart as the origin of both veins and arteries; in this he followed Aristotle, for Galen called the liver the origin of the veins. He was extremely interested in the heart and cardiac valves, but he did not free himself from Galen's view of the passage of blood through the interventricular septum. He studied the cardiac movements in the intact animal by means of an ingenious mechanical device. Finally, he regarded the heart as muscular; in so doing he was less precise than Galen, who wrote that the heart is composed of a special kind of muscular fibres, which are not dependent on nerves.

Omitted from the above account is any survey of da Vinci's views on muscle, nervous system and special senses, etc., but these can readily be found in Franklin, 1949. When we consider the work that da Vinci did in other fields as artist, inventor and so forth, and the degree of excellence which he attained in all of them, we may well be astounded by his discoveries in medical science.

Vesalius (1514–64) was the son of a Belgian father, but his mother was probably English. In 1533, after five years at Louvain, he went to Paris and studied anatomy there under the ardent galenist, Jacobus Sylvius (1478–1555) or Jacques du Bois, and Johannes Guenther (1487–1574) of Andernach. A fellow-prosector of Vesalius was Michael Servetus. In 1536 Vesalius returned to Louvain, but left next year for Venice. In December he was made M.D. of Padua, and entrusted with the duty of conducting public dissections; then or soon afterwards he was appointed professor of surgery with care of anatomy. In 1538 he produced what have since become known as his 'Tabulae anatomicae sex'. In 1539 one of his students, and a lodger in the same house, was Caius, later second founder and Master of Gonville and Caius College, Cambridge. In 1543 Vesalius published at Basel the book which revolutionized anatomy, namely, *De humani corporis fabrica libri septem*. This wonderful and beautifully illustrated book was of importance to physiology in that it gave the first complete and reasonably accurate

31

description of the whole human body. The reception given to it was, however, discouraging and, apart from publishing a second edition in 1555, Vesalius did little further. What he had done was in any case sufficient, for at the age of 28 he had swept away the anatomical authority of over a millennium.

He also made certain more direct contributions to physiology, for in a brief chapter at the end of *De humani corporis fabrica* he gave a concise description of the technique and results of experiments on living animals. 'After accurate study of the anatomy of the cadaver,' he wrote, 'one should proceed to examine the function of organs, or to acquire data from which those functions can be deduced, in the living animal.' *Inter alia*, he showed that the pulsation of arteries is dependent upon the heart and is not an innate quality of these vessels. He noted the presence of pericardial fluid. Finally, by an experiment which gave him more satisfaction than any other, he showed that, if the lungs of an animal were collapsed and the heart brought almost to a standstill, successive artificial inflations of the lungs through a tube tied into the trachea would restore the activity of the heart to normal. The repetition of these and of other experiments described in the chapter mentioned would form an intriguing series of demonstrations in a practical physiology course today. It is, however, necessary to note that most animal experiments before Harvey's time were concerned with the observation of normal function rather than with an experimental questioning of nature as to function. It is difficult to draw the line in any individual case, but the experiments of Vesalius and his predecessors would be more properly called 'zooscopy', or the observation of living animals, than experimental physiology in its modern sense. At the same time, such a technique does give the observer most valuable information about normal function, is an admirable corrective to ideas gathered solely from anatomical dissection, and is still a procedure of use to the physiologist. Zooscopy needs only skilful operation and accurate observation, experimental physiology needs in addition correct interpretation, and the pitfalls which can beset the interpreter can be seen in the subsequent history of the science in question.

To return, however, to Vesalius. He contributed in yet another way, the importance of which cannot be exaggerated, to the advance of physiology. In the first edition of his book he noted that the interventricular septum abounded on both sides with pits, but that not one of these, so far as the senses could perceive, penetrated from the right to the left ventricle. He wondered therefore at the art of the Creator, who caused blood to pass through invisible pores. In the second edition Galen no longer swayed him, he had become completely sceptical, and he did not see how even the smallest particle of blood could be transferred from the right to the left ventricle through the septum. Ibn an-Nafis had reached this point, as we have seen, and gone beyond it three centuries before Vesalius. But the former's views had not, apparently, been retained in the literature used by the medical profession, so Vesalius, in denying the possibility of a passage of blood through the interventricular septum, helped to prepare the way for Harvey.

Other writers in the sixteenth century who were dissatisfied with the traditional teaching about the route taken by blood in its passage from the right to the left side of the heart were Servetus, Columbus, Botallus, and Caesalpinus. For three of these the alternative route of choice was via the artery-like vein [the pulmonary arterial system] to the lungs and via the vein-like artery [the pulmonary venous system] back to the heart; in other words, they unconsciously came to the same conclusion as Ibn an-Nafis had done three centuries earlier, and the judgement passed on his contribution (see above) applies equally to theirs. The fourth writer,

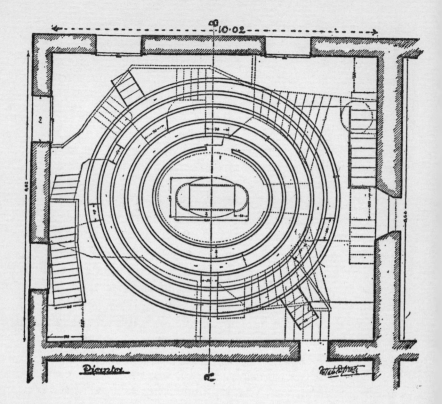

FIGURE I

Architect's drawings made at the suggestion of Charles Singer, and under the direction of Professor Castiglioni. The originals were exhibited at the Harvey Tercentenary celebrations in 1928, and are now in the keeping of the Royal College of Physicians. Figure 1 gives the plan, Figure 2 the elevation (along the dotted line AB of Figure 1), of the anatomical lecture-theatre of Hieronymus Fabricius of Aquapendente. In Figure 1 I have emphasized one actual dimension (10.02 metres between the two arrows) at the top. In Figure 2 I have also emphasized one actual dimension (5.40 metres between the two arrows) at the top on the right.

34

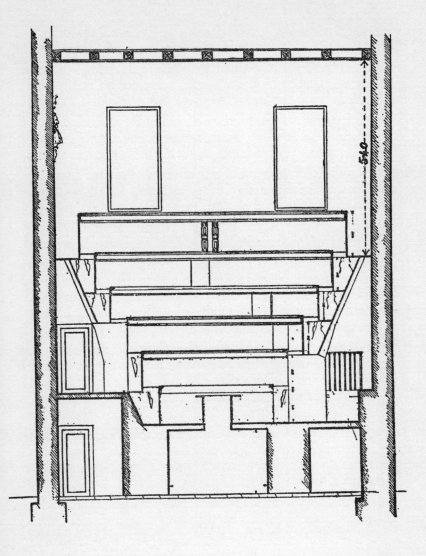

FIGURE 2

Botallus, was misled by fortuitous post-natal persistence of the foetal foramen ovale, and considered this passage to be the regular blood-route from the right to the left side of the heart. None of the four writers had any idea of a circulation of blood in our sense, or advanced any experimental proof of such a contention.

Michael Servetus or Miguel Servet (1509 or 1511–33) was probably born at Vilanova de Xisxena 'in the racial no-man's land between Catalonia and Aragon' (Trueta, 1956), and he became a strange mixture of religious reformer, physician and scholar. From 1535 to 1538 he was in Paris, and there came into contact with Jacobus Sylvius, Guenther of Andernach, and Vesalius. Guenther says that, helped by Vesalius, and 'after him by Michael Villanovanus, distinguished by his literary acquirements of every kind, and scarcely second to any in his knowledge of galenic teaching', he examined the whole body and demonstrated to the students all the muscles, veins, arteries and nerves. Long afterwards, in 1553, Servetus privately printed a thousand copies of a book which he had had in manuscript for at least seven years. This work, called *Christianismi restitutio*, aroused opposition by the heretical views which it contained, and its author was burned alive at the stake in Geneva. Almost all copies of the book were destroyed with Servetus, and maybe a maximum of three, one of them imperfect, are all that still remain. It is in this book that one finds, casually introduced among theological discussions, the first sixteenth-century account of the pulmonary vascular system. In it Servetus stated quite clearly that blood passes from the right to the left side of the heart, not through the interventricular septum but through what we nowadays style the pulmonary artery and vein; in its passage through this long intrapulmonary course it gives up sooty vapours and comes out reddish in colour. That this is the way the blood passes is proved by the communications between pulmonary artery and vein, and by the size of the pulmonary artery, which is far too large for the nutrition of the lungs alone. In the lungs, and not in the heart, air mixes with the blood and it becomes red in colour. Servetus compared this passage from [our] pulmonary artery to pulmonary vein with that from portal vein to vena cava within the liver.

That this break with the traditional view was recorded in so matter-of-fact a way is at first sight very surprising, but it becomes less so when one remembers that it was merely an alternative (if more rational) view about the route taken by a small amount of blood; the main concept of the elaboration of the spirit of life from the interaction of blood and air remained unaffected, though it is of interest that Servetus changed the site of this process from the left ventricle to the lungs. What exactly induced him to think of the pulmonary vascular route we may not, so late as this, ever discover. It is, however, easy to imagine that the idea came to him during his dissecting days in Paris, for a disbelief in Galen's intra-septal pores must have been fairly widespread among those who had the opportunity and the curiosity to examine the heart itself, and who were not bound by tradition. As a stimulus to others the contribution made by Servetus was possibly ineffective, owing to the destruction of all but a few copies of the book. In fact, it became generally known only through Charles Bernard, a surgeon of St Bartholo-mew's Hospital. Bernard brought the passage on the pul-monary system to the notice of William Wotton, who republished it in 1694 in his *Reflections upon ancient and modern learning*.

The next account of the pulmonary system, not unlike that of Servetus, was given by Matthaeus Realdus Columbus (1516–59), and was published posthumously in his *De re anatomica*, 1559. Columbus had been born at Cremona; thereafter he had been at Padua with Vesalius, deputized for him in 1543, and succeeded him in 1544. In 1545 he went as first Professor of Anatomy to Pisa, but left there in 1548 for a chair in Rome, where he stayed until his death. Vesalius was not impressed by Columbus, and regarded him as unlettered and unscientific. Columbus plagiarized the work of Vesalius and of Ingrassiaz in his book, and some have suggested that he acquired his account of the pulmonary system in a similar way, for the manuscript account of Servetus went to Padua as early as 1546. Whatever the facts may be, Columbus claimed to be the first discoverer, his account did become generally accessible, and in it he included the description of the working of the cardiac, pulmonary and aortic valves. It is of interest that he said that *almost* all believed in the passage of blood through the interventricular septum.

The third sixteenth-century contribution occurred in a short work by Leonardus Botallus, who had been born in Italy in 1530 but was of French parentage, and who became Physician to King Charles IX of France. The note, for it is nothing more than that, was published in Paris in 1564 after the author's *De catarrho*, and was republished in Lyons in the following year. In it Botallus claimed to show the way, till then unknown, by which blood passes to the left ventricle. He began by saying that he was led to his discovery by the discrepancy between the accounts given by Galen and by Columbus respectively.[1] After previously attempting without success to check these accounts, he had returned to the task and, while dissecting a calf's heart, had found a fairly wide 'ductus' leading directly into the left auricle from just above the coronary vein [sinus] opening. This 'ductus' or 'vena' could, he wrote, be called the nutrient vessel of the arteries and of the spirits of life, because 'arterial blood' [i.e., blood *for* the arteries or, in a proleptic sense, blood that was to become arterial] was carried through it into the left

[1]Incidentally, he was incomplete in his account of Galen's ideas, and inaccurate in his statement about the findings of Columbus.

38

Hempstead parish church as it was before the tower fell down in 1882. The arrows mark the extent of the building in 1938.

ventricle and thereby into all the arteries. The pathways suggested by Galen and by Columbus were not, therefore, the true ones. The one found by Botallus was fairly large and open in calves, pigs and dogs. In man, on the other hand, it was somewhat smaller and its course was more tortuous; in addition, it was apparently guarded on both sides by valves. Hence, coagulated blood [ordinary venous blood in the right side of the heart was regarded as coagulable] was not encountered in the left ventricle of man, but was so in that of [lower] animals.

Botallus had, obviously, stumbled upon the persistence of the foetal foramen ovale that can occur in the adult mammal; but it was left for Harvey (1628, cap. 6, 55) to put the discovery into its right place in the scheme of things. It is strange that Botallus had no negative findings to report—an uninterrupted series of patent foramina ovalia in the species mentioned is certainly remarkable.

The fourth contribution was that of Andreas Caesalpinus (1519–1603), of Arezzo, who was the first to use the word 'circulatio' and whose writings contain many references to the *movement* of the blood and the *action* of the heart; if these are not presented in a consequent manner (according to Bayon, 1939), it is easy to withdraw sentences from their context and to suggest that Caesalpinus was referring to the circulation as we know it. He wrote *Quaestiones peripateticae* and other books, and in 1655, i.e., during Harvey's lifetime, Harvey's correspondent, Giovanni Nardi of Florence had asserted in his *Noctes geniales* that Caesalpinus had previously described the circulation of the blood. A further examination, however, by Bayon of the relevant text showed that Caesalpinus supported Aristotle's doctrine of the primacy of the heart and simultaneously did not oppose Galen's opinion about the straining of the blood through the perforate interventricular septum of that organ; moreover, Caesalpinus seemed to have attached a different connotation from ours

40

to the word 'circulatio'. Caesalpinus had not been accepted by Fabricius at Padua, and it is, therefore, probable that Harvey did not know of his work, which he did not, certainly, list. It remained unmentioned by Riolan, Bartholin, Jan de Wale, and de Beck, according to Bayon.

Hieronymus Fabricius was born about 1530 in Aquapendente, near Orvieto, about half-way between Rome and Siena, and he went to the University of Padua, then probably the most famous in Italy, about 1550. At this time he was a young man gifted with great powers of memory and a keen and penetrating mind. His prowess in public and in private was beginning to mark him out when he turned his attention to medicine, and in this he was fortunate, for he studied under Gabrielus Falloppius (1523–62), 'the Aesculapius of his age', and an extremely able exponent of his subject. About 1559 Fabricius took his Doctorate of Philosophy and Medicine, and in due course he was appointed professor of surgery with charge of anatomy, i.e., he followed Falloppius. In 1574 he first saw valves in veins during the course of his dissection, and he described at a later date the joy with which he found them ('a me summa cum laetitia inter dissecandum observata fuere'). He intended his book on these structures (*De venarum ostiolis*, 1603) to be one of a series of standard-size anatomy books, but he let Salomon Alberti publish *his* account and figures first, and while Fabricius's book was still evolving William Harvey was away back to England with *his* plans. Fabricius was the creator of comparative anatomy and he left his illustrations of it to the State of Venice to be placed in the library. All the memories of him at Padua are friendly ones, and in embryology he was not only a forerunner of Harvey as regards technique, but also was keenly interested in the subject itself. In the sixteenth century Padua had ten thousand medical students, including a thousand Poles, and, when Fabricius died on Tuesday, 21 May 1619, he was given a magnificent funeral oration by his friend, Johannes Thuilius Mariaemontanus. 'Cecidit, heu cecidit, Hieronymus Fabricius ab Aquapendente, patriae suae decus, Medicinae, lumen, Anatomiae restaurator, Chirurgiae parens, Gymnasii Patavini gloria, imo Universae rei Litterariae commune bonum. Una dies, una hora, unum temporis momentum abstulit, quod saecula non resarcient; praereptus est nobis ille Vir, quem qui aequent, nedum superent, communi omni judicio vix reperiuntur. Lugrant igitur hunc casum communiter omnes, defleant hanc miseriam cives et peregrini, hunc interitum nemo non luctu et planctu prosequatur, et praestantissumum hunc virum hic iacentem conspiciens nullus non effundat uberrima lacrymanum flumina.'

According to Professor C. J. Sisson, who examined material not yet published in the Public Record Office, Thomas Harvey, William's father, was described as Esquire and at the time of his death was living at Hackney, Middlesex. By his own account he was born in 1551, though his birth-date is usually given as 1549; a reproduction of his portrait, at the age of 64 according to the legend, is given as Fig. 1 of Sir Geoffrey Keynes's book, *The Portraiture of William Harvey*. His dates, as given by Munk, are 1549 to 12 June 1623.

He was married twice; by his first wife, Juliana Jenkin, whom he married about 1575, he had a daughter, also named Juliana, who later married Thomas Cullen of Dover and who died about 1639. William Harvey was the first of the nine children of Thomas's second wife, *née* Joan Hawke or Halke, who were all born at Folkestone.

William's birthday was 1 April 1578 and he was thus an Elizabethan. He was followed by Sarah (5 May 1580— 18 June 1591). Then came John (12 November 1582 —20 July 1645), who was called a 'footman' to King James I and later became M.P. for Hythe; he entrusted William with the responsibility of bringing up his son, also John

42

(*see* Cope, 1959). Thomas was born on 17 January 1584–85, married about 1613 Elizabeth Exton and on 10 May 1621 Elizabeth Parkhurst, and had children by both marriages. He was a Turkey merchant and died on 2 February 1622–23. Also a Turkey merchant was Daniel (born 31 May 1587), whose later days were spent on his estate at Combe, near Croydon, Surrey. His fourth son became Sir Daniel Harvey and was our Ambassador at Constantinople, where he died in 1672. His daughter Elizabeth married Heneage Finch, first Earl of Nottingham, from which marriage are descended the Earls of Winchelsea and Aylesford. Yet another Turkey merchant was Eliab (born 26 February 1589–90), the most successful of the brothers, with estates at Rochampton, Surrey, and at Chigwell, Essex. It was he who built the Harvey Mortuary Chapel at Hempstead Church, Essex. He died in 1661. Michael, too, was a Turkey merchant; he had been born on 25 August 1593, and lived at St Laurence, Pountney, and St Helen's, Bishopsgate. Matthew (born 25 August 1593), Michael's twin, was of the same persuasion; he died on 21 December 1642. Finally, there was Amye, who was born on 26 December 1596.

The family was a very united one, and three of his brothers remembered William in their wills. It has sometimes been said that William Harvey was not a good man of business, but Sir Wilmot Herringham did not believe that, and Sir Zachary Cope (1959) and others have shown that much the opposite was in fact the truth.

To go back, however. Not only was Thomas Harvey married successively to Juliana Jenkin and to Joan Halke, but he was partner with the fathers, William Jenkin in a coastal and cross-channel service, and Thomas Halke, a merchant of Canterbury, who operated onwards to London; by about 1580 these men were between them giving considerable help to the Merchant Adventurers of London. On 5 September 1586 Thomas Harvey was elected Mayor of the Cinque Port of Folkestone, and he was ordered to inspect the local preparations for meeting invasion, as well as to render a return of the town's contributions to the Royal Navy in respect of seamen, ships, and stores of powder. In 1587 to 1588 began the struggle named by its most recent chronicler (Mattingly, 1959), 'The defeat of the Spanish Armada', and on 8 July 1588 the Privy Council gave warning that a Spanish fleet was at sea—the local defence forces took up their positions and beacons were lighted. But Sir Francis Drake had already at Cadiz made an attack from 29 April to 1 May 1587, with a loss to the Spanish side of no fewer than twenty-four ships valued at one hundred and seventy-two thousand ducats, together with damage to Philip of Spain's prestige from the daring of the raid, so that Drake said to himself after it that England should look well to the Sussex coast. On 29 July 1588, in sight of Folkestone (Hare, 1957), as the Spanish fleet was battered into defeat, the s.w. wind rose to gale force sweeping the smoke of battle and the remnants of the Armada into the northern seas, whence less than half the fleet returned to Spain.

During that summer Harvey passed the examination in reading, writing, English and Latin for his admission into Canterbury Grammar School (or King's School, Canterbury) as a fee-paying scholar. He was to lodge with his uncle, Thomas Halke, while his father's frequent business visits were continually to remind him of home and of holidays. The durable influences on his boyhood (Hare, 1957) were of persons rather than institutions, of nature's way rather than abstract ideas. From his mother[1] came his charitable disposition and life-long though unobtrusive

[1] '. . . who dyed in ye 50th year of her age, mother of 7 sons and 2 daughters, a goodly harmless woman . . . deere to her husband, reverenced by her children, . . . whose soule rest in heaven.' Inscription on a brass over her flagstone in Folkestone Church.

44

loyalty to the Anglican faith and liturgy. From his father came his vigour, temper, and capacity for hard work and for taking pains. In the vale of Folkestone he found his kinship with the life of the countryside.

At ten years of age he was admitted to the King's School, Canterbury, a very old foundation which had been taken over by King Henry VIII, enlarged, re-endowed, and placed under the Dean and Chapter. There were fifty boys on the foundation, and others who were allowed to come, of whom Harvey was one, though he was a 'commoner'. His schooldays seem to have been not dissimilar to those which he was to have later at Gonville and Caius College as an undergraduate, and it is probable that, by the time he went thither, he could not only read, write and talk Latin, but had a working knowledge of Greek.

In his sixteenth year Harvey, described as the son of Thomas Harvey, yeoman, of Folkestone in the County of Kent, was admitted at Gonville and Caius College, Cambridge, as a scholar (Pensionarius minor), with George Estey, a Fellow of the College and a Lecturer in Hebrew, going surety for him; the date of admission was the last day of May, 1593. Matthew Parker, who had been Master of Corpus Christi College, Cambridge, before he became Archbishop of Canterbury, had founded in 1572 a scholarship which was tenable for six years, together with free lodging and college tuition. Harvey was the only one of the first ten holders who took up medicine, though the conditions were most favourable, namely, three years of study in subjects useful to medicine, followed by three years of medicine itself. Further, the scholars had to be able, learned, and worthy youths born in Kent and educated in Canterbury, while Matthew Parker's benefaction was, according to Dean Hook's statement, made at the request of Caius. It is the first case of a scholarship for medical training (Herringham, 1932, 113).

The student's day began with chapel at 5 (Roughton, 1957), from 6 to 10 there were lectures with a snack of bread and some beer at an interval, a meagre dinner at 10, and then, from 10 to 5 teaching and learning with, at 5, supper 'not much better than dinner' had been. From 6 to 9.30 there was reasoning or other study, and finally for half an hour from 9.30 running to get some heat on the feet before bed. In a word, the day began early and it was all work and no play, rather sparse diet, and not until 1565 any provision of heat. In Queen Elizabeth's reign there began to be some influx of sons of nobles, wealthy men, and merchants, with consequent rise in the standard of living.

Harvey kept his residence well at Caius up to summer 1596, but after that he had many and prolonged absences, some of them due to ill-health. He finally left Cambridge on 30 October 1599, intending to return in January 1600, but the first part of that term found him instead at Padua (Roughton, *ibid.*), and he had presumably passed for the last time into the world through the beautiful Gate of Honour which Caius had had built at his College. Both the University and College separately had provision for public anatomies, and one 'John Figgis so made anatomy at the Schools, and was buried at Great St Mary's Church on the twelfth of March, 1566'. But there is no evidence that Harvey attended any such University dissections, though it is possible that the corpse which he mentioned in his 1616 Lumleian lecture as having been seen at Cambridge had been obtained under the provisions of the Charter given by Queen Elizabeth to Caius College.

In recalling in 1662 Harvey's life at Cambridge, Scarburgh (Payne, 1957) tells of 'the great goodwill, the esteem, and the devotion he excited among those around him: for such was his nature. He devoted himself assiduously to his studies and turned with the greatest zeal to philosophy.

46

After the manner of the ancient philosophers (as they say about Plato and Pythagoras) he thought that he should travel as widely as possible in the hope of acquiring thereby some of their teaching and wisdom. Therefore this genius, who was to become a second Aesculapius, did not continue to remain in this country.' [England.]

'It would seem that while he studied at Padua, and not before, Harvey began to think of his career. He thought again and again and for a long time how he could raise himself effectively from the ground and place his head among the stars and at last there settled in his mind the wish to embrace medicine.' The young Englishman, for whom the thoughts of youth were thus such long, long thoughts, presumably enrolled among the students of Fabricius on St Luke's Day in 1600, when the Paduan medical session began with an oration in praise of medicine, followed by [? for Catholics only] High Mass and the Litany of the Holy Spirit. A certain 'D. Gulielmus Ameius Anglus', who was first in the list of English students in the Jurist University of Padua, was elected as Councillor of the English nation for the years 1600–01 and 1601–02, and the discovery in 1893 of Harvey's 'stemma' for the earlier date showed that 'Ameius' and 'Harveius' were one and the same; a coloured drawing was made for the Royal College of Physicians soon after the stemma had been discovered. The pen-picture Sir Thomas Barlow drew of Harvey as he was in 1600 was 'rather on the small side, with raven hair, dark piercing eyes, somewhat sallow complexion, and a keen restless demeanour and rapid speech'. 'He was a keen and accurate observer and an enthusiastic naturalist, and he had a mind reflective as to the causes and relations of things, fertile in recognizing resemblances, and, above all, ready in making working hypotheses and in devising experiments which would more or less verify those hypotheses.' It was in these latter qualities, says Barlow, that Harvey's supremacy over his teachers and predecessors ultimately became so manifest. The addition of experiment to observation was vital and far reaching.

Dalla Volta (1957), who tried to evoke from the most reliable writings a picture of Paduan life and society at the beginning of the seventeenth century in its cultural, religious and mundane aspects, found that it was in an atmosphere dominated by experimental research rather than by philosophical attitudes that the undergraduate began there his medical studies, and that there was continuous exchange of doctrines and ideas between students and teachers. Harvey was a councillor for two years in the University of the jurists, and had the right to erect a 'stemma', that is, a tablet commemorating his residence and office, in each of two successive years. The University of Padua was the official one of Venice, and it was marked by veneration for learning, religious tolerance [contrast, e.g. Rome, where in 1600 the great Giordano Bruno lost his life at the stake], international spirit, and freedom of thought. In Harvey's time there was an anatomical school on Vesalian lines, with comparative anatomy and embryology added from Aristotle, and experimental physiology reintroduced after its more or less complete abeyance throughout the world since Galen's time, and given an English prudence, thoroughness and patience (Cawadias, 1957). Montanus was the man primarily responsible for the founding of a clinical school where students could practise and note details about their cases, and presumably Harvey had such opportunities at Padua.

The reader should envisage the wonderful permanent anatomical theatre of Fabricius in his mind's eye if he cannot actually see it or the remarkable scale model of it made by Dr E. Ashworth Underwood, Director of the Wellcome Historical Medical Museum, London, N.W.1. The original dates from 1594 and Fabricius began his course in it on 16 January of 1595. It occupied the greater part of the room, and contained six concentric galleries so narrow that

48

spectators had perforce to stand, so little one above the other that the heads in one were only three feet above those in the one below. A tall man could not have stood upright without obscuring the view of the man behind and above him, and the head of the most distant spectator was only twenty-five feet away from the object of demonstration. The theatre held about three hundred people, and a calculation shows that there was just space for this number. In the small oval at the bottom was a table for the body, or the part of it, which was to be dissected, and the space around this was reserved for the Professor of Anatomy, the Rectors of the City, the Rectors of the School, the Councillors and Members of the Medical College, and representatives of the Venetian nobility. Reference to the plans of the building (Franklin, 1933, Figs. 5 and 6) will show that these dignitaries cannot simultaneously have been present in any large number. The first gallery was occupied by the Councillors of the Nations (into which many medieval universities were divided), and the ones above by students. The theatre which had no windows was lighted only by two candelabra, each having three candles, and by eight lamps held by that number of students.

Harvey's diploma as Doctor of Medicine of the University of Padua found its way to the Royal College of Physicians of London on 7 July 1766 after the publication of his *Opera omnia* by the College. It was a gift from the then Headmaster of the King's School, Canterbury, and recalls the 'stemma' or commemorative tablet erected in the Cloisters of the University of Padua. The diploma sets out the praiseworthy accomplishments of the diplomate, and was confirmed by the seal of the Universitas artistarum of Padua and of Count Sigismund as Count Palatine. The document is closed by a list of witnesses, including Simeon Fox, who later became President of the College of Physicians, and Sir Matthew Lister, Physician-in-Ordinary to King Charles I. But most interesting of all is the signature of Hieronymus Fabricius of Aquapendente, who in 1600 must have been preparing for the publication of his book *De venarum ostiolis*, or little flood-gates in veins. This work contained a passage in which Fabricius wrote: 'That the blood flow is slowed by the valves, evident even without this from their actual construction, can be tested by anyone either in the exposed veins of the cadaver, or in the living subject if he passes a ligature round the limbs as in blood-letting. For, if one tries to exert pressure on the blood, or to push it along by rubbing from above downwards, one will clearly see it held up and delayed by the valves. This indeed is the way in which I was led to an observation of such nature. Small veins, however, had no need of valves, for two reasons. First, owing to their smallness, they held only a little blood and all that suffices for them: and secondly, it was sufficient for the nutriment to delay in the larger vessels as in a fountain-head, since by this means the smaller tributaries would not lack what was necessary.' Had Fabricius understood things better, he could and should have seen the evidence for a forward direction of blood movement throughout the cardio-vascular system and so have anticipated his pupil, William Harvey, in his momentous discovery.

It is very relevant to ask how the latter saw so clear a line of research ahead of him, and I must begin by expressing my belief that his research principles remained constant through his life, so that one can still find much use in reading two sections from *De generatione animalium*. Also, his embryological work was begun in Padua with Fabricius, even if the account of it as a whole was not sent by Dr Ent to the press until half a century later. 'Careful observation,' Harvey wrote, 'is needed in every discipline, and sensation itself is often to be consulted. One's own experience is to be relied upon, not that of someone else.' Just after that he said that we were to judge by our seeing rather than to believe anything which he *wrote* about the generation of animals. 'For all true knowledge depends upon beginnings deriving from sensory investigation, and special care must be taken that you know these things well and have investigated them through frequent dissections of animals. . . In this rank age there are many who write and argue speciously, but few who are truly wise and philosophers. I have thought fit to offer you this foretaste of what is to come so that you may know the assistance on which I have relied, and the advice which I have followed, in making these experiments and observations of mine public knowledge . . . so that you yourselves, treading in the same tracks, may not only judge impartially but, deserting clevernesses and probable guesses and keeping to what you can see for yourselves, may discover very many things as yet unknown to others, and certainly rather outstanding.'

'All men,' says Aristotle, the leading dictator of philosophy, 'naturally wish to know. The sign of this is the pleasure which they get from using their senses, among which I choose as the outstanding one that of vision, because this is the one most conducive to our knowledge of anything and makes plain many differences' . . . 'The research method in use today is quite unsuitable and misleading, since very many inquire not what things are, but what is said about them by others' . . . 'I therefore whisper in your ear, friend Reader, that you weigh in the exact balance of experience whatever I treat of in these essays . . . that indeed you use them only in so far as you find them most firmly corroborated by the direct evidence of your own senses.'

Long ago, in 1933, I quoted from the Hon. Robert Boyle the passage in which he wrote about Harvey's memory of the reasons that induced him to think of a circulation of the blood. 'He answer'd me that when he took notice that the Valves in the Veins of so many several Parts of the Body, were so Plac'd that they gave free passage to the Blood

Towards the Heart, but oppos'd the passage of the Venal Blood the Contrary way: He was invited to imagine, that so Provident a Cause as Nature had not so Plac'd so many Valves without Design: and no Design seem'd more probable, then that, since the Blood could not well, because of the interposing Valves, be sent by the Veins to the Limbs: it should be Sent through the Arteries, and Return through the Veins, whose Valves did not oppose its course that way' (Boyle, R., 1688.)

Drs Hunter and Macalpine have recently (1958) made a most painstaking survey of this and of all the other passages in which Harvey is mentioned in Boyle's works, a total of twenty-five quotations which are of considerable total biographical interest, together with a note written to Boyle by Samuel Hartlib, dated Charing Cross 30 June 1657, telling him of Harvey's death: 'In the time I need not tell you, that the most learned famous English Aesculapius (I mean Dr *Harvey*) is departed this world.'

In addition to the 1688 reference, already given, I will quote here No. 5 from p. 119 of the 1958 paper. 'The next attribute of God,' it reads, 'that shines forth in his creatures, is his wisdom . . . Thus the circular motion of the blood, and structure of the valves of the heart and veins (the consideration whereof, as he himself told me, first hinted the circulation to our famous *Harvey*) though now modern experiments have for the main (the modus seeming yet not so fully explicated) convinced us of them: yet those many learned anatomists, that have for many succeeding ages preceded both Dr Harvey and Columbus, Caesalpinus, Padre Paulo [Paolo Sarpi], and Mr Warner [Walter Warren] (for each of these last four are supposed by some to have had some knowledge of the circulation) by all their diligent contemplation of human bodies, never dreamed (for aught appears) of so advantageous an use of the valves of the heart, nor that nimble circular motion of the blood, of which our modern circulators think they discern such excellent use, not to say, necessity.'

After he had taken his doctorate of medicine at Padua on 25 April 1602, Harvey must have continued working on embryological or cardiovascular studies for some time, but he returned fairly soon to Cambridge to incorporate there as doctor in the same faculty. For, though the Paduan degree allowed him to practise in England, he needed the *ad eundem* one to become eligible in time for the Fellowship of the College of Physicians. We need to make reasonable working suppositions where we have not complete facts, and my hypothesis is that his new idea of the way the blood moves had come to Harvey in the anatomical theatre at Padua while he attended a demonstration by Fabricius, that on consideration he had found it satisfying so far as it went, and that thereafter it became his chief scientific preoccupation, though the tasks of earning his living and of advancing in his profession were understandably not neglected. During the year in which he so began, England and Scotland were united in the person of King James I of the former country, and of King James VI of the latter one, through the death of the great Queen Elizabeth. *De venarum ostiolis*, the short but handsomely illustrated book by Fabricius on little floodgates in the veins, was produced, too, from the press of Laurentius Pasquatus in that year, 1603.

After his incorporation as M.D. at Cambridge in 1602, Harvey lost very little time in applying for admission to the College of Physicians, his first appearance being on 4 May 1603. Although his replies to all questions were entirely satisfactory, he was not immediately allowed to proceed with his other examinations, but was nevertheless given permission to practise. Though supported by Dr Lancelot Browne, who had been first Physician to Queen Elizabeth, he was unsuccessful in his application for the post of Physician to the Tower, the Physician, Dr Elvey, being then very ill. He next appeared for examination at the College in April 1604, and after further appearances was finally admitted a Candidate on 5 October; on 24 November 1604 he married in St Sepulchre's Church, Holborn, Elizabeth Browne, daughter of the just-mentioned Lancelot Browne, who was dead on 11 December 1605, more or less at the same time as Harvey's mother, Joan, to whom reference has already been made. We know little about Elizabeth Harvey, but the portrait of her which used to be at Burley-on-the-Hill, near Oakham, showed her 'to have been tall, of a dark complexion and a somewhat severe aspect'— (Norman Moore, 1901) [this picture was destroyed in a fire in ?1908]. Harvey was elected Fellow of the College on 16 May 1607 (Barlow, 1916) or 5 June (D'Arcy Power, 1897), and began an active association with it that ended only at his death.

In 1608, when he was thirty, he brought to the Governors of St Bartholomew's Hospital letters of recommendation from King James I, on receipt of which these Governors loyally elected him to be 'Physician in Reversion' or, as we should now say, Assistant Physician. Dr Wilkinson, the Physician, died in late summer, 1609, and Harvey became Physician, an office which he held until 1643. His charge read as follows, and it is of note that he exercised a greater influence than any medical officer before the time of Abernethy. Especially is this so in regard to the rules drawn up for the admission and government of the patients, and for the duties of the medical officers, drawn up—one gathers— by Harvey himself.

'14th October, 1609

The Chardge of the Phisicon of St Bartholomew's Hospitall.

Phisicon:

You are here elected and admitted to be the Phisicon

54

for the Poore of this hospitall, to p'forme the chardge following. That is to say, one day in the weeke at the leaste thorough the yeare, or offtner as neede shall requyer you shall come to this Hospitall, and cause the Hospitler, Matron, or Porter, to call before you in the hall of this hospitall such and soe many of the poore harboured in this hospitall, as shall neede the counsell and advise of the phisicon. And you are here requyred by us, in God his most holy name, that you endevour yourself to do the beste of your knowledge in the profession of phisicke to the poore then p'sente, or any other of the poore at any tyme in the weeke wch shalbe sent home unto you by the Hospitler or Matron for your counsell, wrytinge in a book appoynted for that purpose, such medicines with their compoundes and necessaries as apperteyneth to the apothecary of this house, to be provyded and made reddy to be ministred unto the poore, every one in p'ticular, according to his disease. You shall not for favour, lucre or gaine, appoynte or write any thing for the poore, but such good and wholesome things as you shall thinke wth your best advise will doe the poore good, without any affeccon or respecte to be had to the apothecary. And you shall take noc gift or reward of any of the poore of this house for your counsell. This you will promise to doe as you shall answeare before God, and as it becometh a faithfull phisicon, whom you ought cheifly to serve, on this vocation, is by God called unto, and for your negligence herein, if you faile you shall render accompte. And soe we requyer you faithfully to promise in God his most holly name, to p'forme this chardge in the hearinge of us, with your beste endeavour as God shall enable you soe long as you shalbe phisicon to the poore of this hospitall; Provided alwaies yt if any patient now admitted or hereafter to bee admitted shalbee soe infirme of body, yt hee, shee, or they cannot p'sonally come into the hall without p'judice to their healthes That then at all tymes in such cases haveing notice you shall goe into such ward or wards in this house to p'scribe for their diseases.'

In 1582 the Lumleian Lectures of the College of Physicians had been founded by Richard Caldwell, a former President of the College, and by Lord Lumley (1534–1609), whose Library, with the help of his brother-in-law, Humphrey Lloyd, private physician to Lord Arundel, trebled in size and in 1590 had none superior in England to it for the study of any of the sciences. In 1613, in the November of which year Fabricius finally retired from teaching at Padua after fifty years, Harvey was elected Censor of the College, an office which he was to hold for second and third times in 1625 and 1629 respectively. The Censors were four Fellows appointed yearly with power to supervise, watch, correct and govern those who practised physic in London or within a seven miles' radius of it, whether or not they were members of the College. Together with representatives of the Society of Apothecaries they made inquisitorial visits at irregular times in summer and in autumn to the shops of apothecaries in London. According to Sir Humphrey Rolleston, Henry Power (1623–68) in 1652 and, therefore, during Harvey's lifetime (in a section of British Museum MS. Sloane 1343) wrote of 'Circulatio harveiana inventa ab authore A.D. 1614', thereby antedating by two years the earliest known reference to that discovery. Harvey was in 1615, in fact, appointed to the Lumley and Caldwell Lectureship on Anatomy and Surgery in the College of Physicians. The appointment was supposed to be for life, but Harvey gave it up in favour of Charles Scarburgh in 1656. On Tuesday, Wednesday, and Thursday, 16, 17, and 18 April 1616 he gave three Lumleian Lectures, and the seventeen inches long whalebone rod which he is said to have used is preserved at the College of Physicians. In the

Wednesday Lecture (see *Praelectiones anatomiae universalis*, p. 80) is the transcript of the relevant page of notes by Harvey, which states in a Latin-English mélange:

> W.H. constat per fabricam cordis sanguinem
> per pulmones in Aortam perpetuo
> transferri, as by two clacks of a
> water bellows to rayse water
> constat per ligaturam transitum sanguinis
> ab artery's ad venas
> unde △ perpetuum sanguinis motum
> in circulo fieri pulsu cordis
> an ?hoc gratia nutritionis
> an magis Conservationis sanguinis
> et Membranorum per Infusionem calidam
> viccisimque sanguinis Calefaciens
> membra frigifactum a Corde
> Calefit.

The notes are, one hears, to be superseded shortly by a new transcript which Professor C. D. O'Malley has in the press, and it would be a work of supererogation on my part to translate the passage quoted, so it suffices to rephrase Boyle's words that Harvey referred his discovery of the circulation of the blood to 'contrivances similar to the valves used in hydraulic engines for producing counter currents (Barlow, 1957, 1266). Bayon (1951), however, said that whether Harvey was persuaded of the true facts of the circulation by mathematical, Aristotelian or any other method of reasoning, it was obvious to himself, Bayon, that Harvey, having noted the heart in action outside and inside the body, gradually conceived the logical sequence, helped by knowledge of the function of the valves in the veins, which brought him to understand how the blood circulated continuously'.

It is pertinent about this point to mention the anatomical

tables preserved in the College and formerly supposed to have been those used by Harvey in his lectures. They had long been preserved at Burley-on-the-Hill, the seat of the Earl of Winchelsea, one of whose ancestors married a niece of Harvey. It has, however, since been shown that they were much more likely to have been the property of Sir John Finch, who was once a Professor of Anatomy at Pisa, and seems to have had for an anatomical pupil one Marchetti, who made 'tables of veins, nerves, and arteries, five times more exact than are described in any author'.

John Evelyn in his *Diary* also refers to some tables which Sir Charles Scarburgh had seen and was anxious that Evelyn should present to the College. He only agreed to lend them for a short time for Scarburgh's use in his lectures, and ultimately presented them to the Royal Society. Evelyn had purchased these tables at Padua in 1646 and had had them transported to England. They were then 'the first of that kind ever seene in our Country, & for ought I know in the World, though afterwards there were others'. The fact that Scarburgh succeeded Harvey as Lumleian Lecturer in 1656 and refers to these tables as 'unique' makes it unlikely that Harvey had used anything of the kind; otherwise his friend Scarburgh would surely have seen them and would not then have regarded Evelyn's as unique.

From 1616 to 1628 there were no objections at the College of Physicians to Harvey's new ideas except on the part of Dr James Primrose (whose date of decease is given by Munk as 1659, and who accepted Galen as authoritative, one of his arguments being that in the olden days patients were healed without the knowledge of the circulation, and that therefore this doctrine, even if true, would be useless. Lint, 1926). Shakespeare died on 23 April 1616, while on 3 February 1618 Harvey was appointed Physician to King James I, and on 7 May of that year was described in *Pharmacopoeia Londinensis*, on the Committee dealing with which he had been

58

serving, as 'Medicus Regius juratus'; in February 1620 he served with Sir Theodore de Mayerne (1573–1654/5) and William Clement on a Committee to watch the surgeons, and in March 1625 he and his brother, John, were admitted Members of Gray's Inn. In that month he attended King James I in the latter's last illness which, in the accusation of the Duke of Buckingham by the House of Commons in the following year, was said to have been connected with a plaster and a posset, administered in 'transcendent presumption' by the Duke. On Harvey's evidence, however, there was nothing harmful in the posset, though he did not advise the plaster because he did not know its ingredients. He was in this year elected Censor of the College for the second time.

In the following year he was offered an official residence in the precincts of Bart's, where many notable people lived, but refused it and received instead an increase in annual salary from £25 to £33 6s. 8d. In 1627 he served on a Committee, appointed by the College of Physicians at the request of the Privy Council, to report on some alum works in St Botolph's, Aldgate, which the Committee condemned as a nuisance. In November Harvey became an Elect of the College vice Gwynne, deceased, after Mayerne had refused because he was too constantly employed at Court.

The former's De motu locali animalium, 1627, written in his own hand, had formed ff. 69–118 of the British Museum Manuscript Sloane 486, and appears to be a previously unpublished notebook in which he jotted down his thoughts with a view, eventually, to publishing a book on animal movement. It was added to at intervals without being finally drafted, and it is this incomplete synopsis which was in 1959 published by the Cambridge University Press after it had been edited, translated and introduced by Dr Gweneth Whitteridge, Archivist to St Bartholomew's Hospital, for the Royal College of Physicians. It appears that Harvey planned a treatise on the movement of muscles even while he was preparing *De motu cordis et sanguinis*. *De motu locali animalium* is the work mentioned in Chapter XVII of the former's essay of 1628, and it shows, even if it contains no new experimental observations, that Harvey's understanding of muscle and of muscular contraction was sounder than that of his predecessors and even of some of his successors.

In 1628, the year in which he turned fifty, he was elected Treasurer of the College of Physicians and also published his first book, entitled, *Exercitatio anatomica de motu cordis et sanguinis*. It seems reasonable to suggest that William Fitzer, the English publisher of the book in Frankfurt, had been suggested by Harvey's friend, Robert Fludd, or Robertus de Fluctibus (1574–1637), second son of Queen Elizabeth's one-time Treasurer of War, and the MS. which he received has been described as 'the most important medical work ever written', for it contained Harvey's 'new concept of the heart's movement and function and of the blood's passage round the body'; this he had confirmed in the presence of the President (Dr Argent) and Fellows of the College of Physicians for more than nine years past by numerous ocular demonstrations, and had freed from the objections of learned and skilful anatomists. In so doing he had surely shown the world 'the truth that is more beautiful than the evening and the morning stars', and had raised himself effectively from the ground and placed his head among the stars, as he had planned to do in his days at Padua.

It is fitting before reading the 'libellus aureus' to cast one's mind back over the efforts of the great men of the past in physiology, and to realize what a supreme act of courage it must have been on the fifty-year-old Harvey's part to challenge concepts established over so many generations. One can understand how much his colleagues at the College must have helped by their agreement with the ocular demonstrations of those things for the reasonable acceptance of which he once again so strongly pressed. 'Over many years a countless succession of distinguished and learned men had followed and illumined a particular line of thought, and this book of mine', he said, 'was the only one to oppose tradition and to assert that the blood travelled along a previously unrecognized circular pathway of its own.' So he was very much afraid of a charge of over-presumptuousness had he let his book, in other respects completed some years earlier, either be published at home or go overseas for printing unless he had first put his thesis before the Fellows and confirmed it by visual demonstration, replied to their doubts and objections, and received the President's vote in favour. He concluded his words to the President and Fellows with a splendid passage worthy of an Elizabethan, which by birth he was: 'It was, however, dear Colleagues,' he said, 'no intention of mine, in listings and upturnings of anatomical authors and writers, to make display by this book of my memory, studies, much reading, and a large printed tome. In the first place, because I propose to learn and to teach anatomy not from books but from dissections, not from the tenets of Philosophers but from the fabric of Nature. Secondly, because I consider it neither fair nor worth the effort to defraud a predecessor of the honour due to him, or to provoke a contemporary. Nor do I think it honourable to attack or fight those who excelled in Anatomy and were my own teachers. Further, I would not willingly charge with falsehood any searcher after truth, or besmirch any man with a stigma of error. But without ceasing I follow truth only, and devote all my effort and time to being able to contribute something pleasing to good men and appropriate to learned ones, and of service to literature.'

In an introduction to his short book of seventy-two pages, Harvey shows the relative weakness of previous accounts of the movement and function of the heart and arteries, for by reading what his predecessors have written and by noting the general trend of opinion handed on by them a man can confirm their correct statements and 'through anatomical dissection, manifold experiments, and persistent careful observation emend their wrong ones.' At the end of his introduction he wrote that 'from these and very many other arguments it is clear that the statements made hitherto by earlier writers about the movement and function of the heart and arteries appear incongruous or obscure or impossible when submitted to specially careful consideration. It will therefore be very useful to look a little more deeply into the matter, to contemplate the movements of the arteries and of the heart not only in man, but also in all other animals with hearts; moreover, by frequent experiments on animals and much use of our own eyes, to discern and investigate the truth.'

In Chapter One he gives his strong reasons for writing, beginning by saying how difficult he found it to discover through the use of his own eyes in living animals the function and offices of the heart's movement so that he all but thought with Fracastorius, that it had been understood by God alone. At length he propounded his new view on the matter, and found it acceptable to some, to others less so. He published so that, if something accrued to the republic of letters through his work in this field, it might perhaps be acknowledged that he had done rightly; also, that others might see that he had not lived idly; or at least that others, given such lead and relying on more productive talents, might find an opportunity to carry out the task more accurately and to investigate more skilfully.

In Chapter Two he gauged the nature of the heart's movements from the dissection of living animals, showing how these movements alternate with rests and are seen best in cold animals or in flagging warmer ones. At the time of its movement the heart becomes generally constricted, its walls thicken, its ventricles decrease in volume and it expels its content of blood, appearing paler in so doing in animals such as serpents, frogs, and the like.

At one and the same time, therefore, occur the beat of the apex, the thickening of the heart walls, and the forcible expulsion of their contained blood by the contraction of the ventricles.

Going on in Chapter Three to the movement of the arteries, likewise gauged from the dissections of living animals, Harvey noted that contraction of the heart and the apex beat occur in systole, simultaneously with dilatation of the arteries and of the artery-like vein, and expulsion of the ventricular content. Arterial pulsation disappears with cessation of ventricular contraction. During cutting or puncture of the ventricles, there is often forcible expulsion of blood from the wound.

Arterial diastole is thus synchronous with cardiac systole but, when movement of blood through arteries is hindered by compression, infarction or interception, the more distal arteries pulsate less because their pulse is nothing other than the impulse of the blood entering them.

Chapter Four dealt with the nature of the movement of the ventricles and of the auricles, gauged from dissection of living animals. [In four-chambered hearts] there are four movements which are distinct in respect of place but not of time, the two auricles moving synchronously and then likewise the two ventricles. With everything more sluggish as the heart lies a-dying, and in fishes and in relatively cold-blooded animals, the auricular and ventricular movements become separated by an interval of inactivity so that the heart appears to respond ever more slowly to the pulsating auricles, and the order of cessation of beating is left ventricle, left auricle, right ventricle, and finally (as Galen noticed) right auricle. 'And while the heart is slowly dying, one can sometimes see it—so to speak—rouse itself and, in reply to two or three auricular beats, produce a single ventricular one slowly and reluctantly and with an effort.' When the heart ceases to beat with the auricle still continuing, digital palpation still enables one to feel the individual auricular pulsations in the ventricles and, if at this time the apex is cut off with a pair of scissors, blood flows out of the wound with each auricular beat, i.e., it is the auricular driving force which gets the blood into the ventricles. At the beats of the auricles and ventricles, which are in fact contractions, there is paling of the chambers concerned; in univentricular animals, there is first contraction of a sort of bladder [?=auricle] at the base of the heart and thereafter ventricular movement. After Harvey had moistened it with saliva and warmed it, a dove's heart which had stopped beating resumed movement and was recalled—so to speak—from death to life. When all regular movement of the heart chambers has ceased, an obscure undulation or palpitation can continue within the right auricular blood itself so long as it retains warmth. 'Hence that which appears last in animals fails first and what appears first fails last.'

In almost all animals a heart is present, though in the bloodless ones it beats very slowly and at long intervals and like the heart of other animals that are a-dying. In some animals in winter and in the cold season there is no pulsation, but they seem to live like plants and are therefore called 'plant-animals'. A heart which has two ventricles always has two auricles, but the reverse is not equally true. A certain throbbing vesicle alone represents the heart in some developing animals, and in the hen's egg, at four or five days from incubation, the beating heart alternated between a red point during relaxation and nothing visible during the rest of the time.

Altogether a grand chapter!

From various observations Harvey believed (Chapter Five) that the movement of the heart begins with the auricles contracting and forcing their contained blood into the ven-

Jean Riolan: from the engraved title-page of *Anthropographia et osteo-logia*, Paris, 1626.

Left: Thomas Howard, 2nd Earl of Arundel and Surrey. *Right:* Charles I; from an engraving by Wenceslaus Hollar.

tricles, which raise themselves, tense, contract and beat, so ejecting into the artery-like vein and aorta respectively the blood received from the corresponding auricles. The movements of the two auricles, on the one hand, and of the two ventricles on the other, appear to happen in rapid succession and give the impression that only one movement is seen, especially in warmer animals in rapid action. 'This,' said Harvey in one of his non-stop passages, 'is comparable with what happens in machines in which, with one wheel moving another, all seem to be moving at once. It also recalls that mechanical device fitted to firearms in which, on pressure to a trigger, a flint falls and strikes and advances the steel, a spark is evolved and falls upon the powder, the powder is fired and the flame leaps inside and spreads, and the ball flies out and enters the target; all these movements, because of their rapidity, seeming to happen at once as in the wink of an eye.' There is a similar sequence of rapid movements in swallowing and a transmission of blood from the veins into the arteries. The heart's one role is such transmission of blood and its propulsion, by means of the arteries, to the extremities everywhere, the aorta being a vessel suitable to dispense blood, which has now reached its absolute perfection, from the heart to the whole of the body. Harvey had earlier disproved the supposed intra-septal pathway from the right ventricle to the left one. So now a new one must be prepared and opened, the discovery of which would ensure that no difficulty existed to prevent 'the admission of those things which he, Harvey, had earlier proposed (about the pulse of the heart and the arteries, the passage of blood from the veins to the arteries, and the distribution of the blood to the whole of the body through the arteries). This leads on to Chapter Six, 'the ways in which the blood is carried from the vena cava into the arteries, or from the right ventricle of the heart into the left one.'

'As the number of animals without lungs,' he began,

'exceeds the number of those with them, and as similarly the number of animals with only one ventricle of the heart exceeds the number of those with two ventricles, it is easy to decide that in the majority of animals, for the most part and on the whole, the blood is transmitted by an obvious route from the veins to the arteries through the chambers of the heart.' 'The same very obviously holds good in the embryos of animals that have lungs, for the two foetal cardiovascular unions are not for the nutrition of the lungs or connected with any inactivity of the heart: further, Botallus was wrong in his finding of a new passage from the vena cava into the left ventricle, for the two foetal unions simultaneously carry blood from the vena cava to the root of the aorta and hence to the arterial system rising from it.

'Thus in the embryo, while the lungs are idle and devoid of activity or movement, as though they did not exist, Nature uses the two ventricles of the heart as one for the transmission of the blood. And the condition of an embryo that has lungs, but is not as yet making use of them, is similar to that of the animal that has no lungs at all.'

'I maintain,' he ended, 'that in the more perfect and warmer animals, and full-grown ones at that (as in man) the blood definitely permeates from the right ventricle of the heart through the artery-like vein into the lungs, thence through the vein-like artery into the left auricle, thence again into the left ventricle of the heart. I maintain, first, that this can happen; secondly, that it has so happened.'

Chapter Seven dealt with the fact that the blood permeates from the right ventricle of the heart through the parenchyma of the lungs into the vein-like artery [pulmonary vein] and the left ventricle. It is simplest to give Harvey's own summary: 'Thus that which dissection establishes as occurring through very wide passages in the majority of animals, and certainly in all animals before they are fully developed, is equally well established as occurring . . . in these fully

66

developed animals through the invisible porosities of their lungs and the minute connections of the lung vessels. From which it is clear that one ventricle of the heart (namely, the left one) would suffice to distribute the blood through the body, and to withdraw it from the vena cava (which indeed is the way it happens in all lungless creatures). When, however, Nature wished the blood to be filtered through lungs, She was forced to make the extra provision of a right ventricle so that its pulsation would drive the blood through these aforesaid lungs from the vena cava to the region of the left ventricle. Thus one has to regard this ventricle as having been made for the lungs and the transfer of blood, and not merely for nutrition. It is altogether incongruous to suppose that the lungs need for their nourishment so large a supply of blood, so pulsatorily delivered, and also so much purer and more spirituous (as being supplied direct from the cardiac ventricles). For they cannot need much more than does the extremely pure substance of the brain, or the very fine and ineffable fabric of the eyes, or the flesh of the heart itself (which is more directly nourished through the coronary artery).'

In Chapter Eight Harvey says that the amount and source of the blood crossing from the veins into the arteries, though worthy of consideration, are so novel and hitherto unmentioned that he fears that in speaking of them he may not only suffer from the ill-will of a few, but dreads lest all men turn against him. 'However, the die has now been cast, and my hope lies in the love of truth and the clear-sightedness of the trained mind.' He tried to assess how much blood was transmitted and in how short a space of time, and noted that the juice of the ingested food could not supply this amount without the veins, on the one hand, being completely emptied and the arteries, on the other hand, being brought to bursting through excessive inthrust of blood, unless that blood somehow flowed back again from the arteries into the veins and returned to the right ventricle of the heart. In consequence, he began privately to consider if it had a movement, as it were, in a circle, and subsequently he verified this hypothesis, finding that the pulsation of the left ventricle forces the blood out of it and propels it through the arteries into all parts of the body's system in exactly the same way as the pulsation of the right ventricle forces the blood out of that chamber and propels it through the artery-like vein into the lungs; finding, further, that the blood flows back again through the veins and the vena cava and right up to the right auricle in exactly the same way as it flows back from the lungs through the so-called vein-like artery to the left auricle (as already described). 'I have,' he said, 'as much right to call this movement of the blood circular as Aristotle had to say that the air and rain emulate the circular movement of the heavenly bodies.'

The Ninth to the Eleventh Chapters are headed, 'The existence of a blood circuit' proved by three suppositions, the fact which they advocate automatically following and the truth being plain to all. The first supposition is that the blood is continuously and uninterruptedly transmitted from the vena cava into the arteries by the heart-beat in too great an amount to be supplied by the ingesta, and thus the whole mass of the blood passes from the vena cava into the arteries in a short space of time.

The second supposition is that the blood is continuously, evenly, and uninterruptedly driven by the arterial beat into every member and part, entering in far greater amount than is nutritionally necessary or can be supplied to it without such rapid circular movement by the whole mass of the blood.

The third supposition is that the veins themselves are constantly returning this blood from each and every member to the heart.

In Chapter Ten the first supposition, about the amount of

blood crossing through the heart from the veins into the arteries, and the existence of a circuit of the blood, is defended from objections and is further confirmed by experiments, including the evidence one can get from one's eyes by opening up a live snake, interrupting the course of the caval blood some distance below the heart and seeing how the part of vein between the ligature and the heart becomes slowly smaller and weaker. On the other hand, once the ligature is released conditions soon revert to normal.

In Chapter Eleven the second supposition is confirmed, and the effects of a medium tight ligature which interrupts the passage of the blood in the veins only is contrasted with that of a tight ligature which interrupts the passage of the blood not only in the veins but also in the arteries. Harvey himself once fell from his carriage and struck his forehead at the point where an arterial branch passed forward from the temples. Within the time of about twenty pulses from the receipt of the blow, he developed a swelling the size of an egg, without either heat or much pain.

In Chapter Twelve the existence of a circuit of the blood is proved by confirmation of the second supposition, and in Chapter Thirteen the third supposition is confirmed, and from it the existence of a circuit of the blood is proved.

Then in Chapter Fourteen he concluded his description of the circuit of the blood by saying, 'May I now be permitted to summarize my view about the circuit of the blood, and to make it generally known?

'Since calculations and visual demonstrations have confirmed all my suppositions, to wit, that the blood is passed through the lungs and the heart by the pulsation of the ventricles, is forcibly ejected to all parts of the body, therein steals into the veins and the porosities of the flesh, flows back everywhere through those very veins from the circumference to the centre, from small veins into larger ones, and thence comes into the vena cava and to the auricle of the heart; all

this, too, in such amount and with so large a flux and reflux
—from the heart out to the periphery, and back from the
periphery to the heart—that it cannot be supplied from the
ingesta, and is also in much greater bulk than would suffice
for nutrition.

'I am obliged to conclude that in animals the blood is
driven round a circuit with an unceasing, circular sort of
movement, that this is an activity or function of the heart
which it carries out by virtue of its pulsation, and that in
sum it constitutes the sole reason for that heart's pulsatile
movement.'

Chapter Fifteen is headed 'The circuit of the blood is
confirmed by probable reasons. As death is a corruption for
lack of warmth and all living things are warm, dying ones
cold, there must be a site and source of warmth to act as the
source from which warmth and life may flow to all parts and
aliment accrue, and upon which digestion, nutrition, and all
activity may depend. That this site is the heart, and that the
heart is the beginning of life in the way which I have stated,
I would have no one doubt . . . It is possible, provided the
heart has remained unaffected, for all the other parts to be
restored to life and recover their health. If, on the other
hand, the heart has been chilled or affected by some serious
fault, then the whole animal must suffer destruction because
its chief organ does so . . . In addition, the heart alone is so
sited and arranged that it can, by its pulsation, impartially
dispense and distribute blood from itself to all parts according to the relative dimensions of their supply arteries, and
thus—so to speak—give freely from its source of wealth to
those in need. Finally, in order that it may leave its central
point and enter narrow and cold parts, the blood needs both
vehemence and an agent to produce it. The only such agent
is the heart, and that in the way that I have stated.'

Chapter Sixteen says that 'The circuit of the blood is
proved from certain consequences'. There are in addition

questions, consequent so to speak upon the supposition of this truth, which are not without their use in establishing belief, as it were a posteriori. When I finally reckon up the number of questions that can be settled, doubts resolved, and obscure places made clear, given this illuminating truth ... I find a field of such vast extent that, if I explored it fully in all directions, not only would this treatise of mine turn, contrary to my plan, into a full-size book, but the rest of my life would perhaps not suffice for my writing of it.'

Finally, Chapter Seventeen states that 'the circuitous movement of the blood is confirmed by things seen within the heart and revealed by anatomical dissection.' There is too much material, however, to précis, including references to the papillary muscles and the heart valves and the pulmonary vessels. Two final questions are, first, 'Why does the artery-like vein, as it is commonly called, have the structure of an artery and the vein-like artery that of a vein?' The answer is that, contrary to general belief, the former is in truth an artery, and the latter a vein, both functionally and structurally and indeed in every respect. The second query is, 'Why has the artery-like vein so wide an opening?' And the answer to it is, 'Because it carries much more than is necessary for the nutrition of the lungs.'

This wonderful book closes with a resounding declaration that 'All these phenomena to be seen during dissection, and very many others, appear if rightly assessed to elucidate well and to confirm fully the truth which I stated earlier in it, and at the same time to oppose the commonly accepted views. For it is very difficult for anyone to explain in any other way than I have done the reason why all these things have been arranged and carried into effect in the manner that I have described.'

In 1628 Harvey was re-elected Treasurer of the College of Physicians but on 3 December of that year, after a splendid feast, 'post splendidum convivium', he asked permission of the President and the Elects to resign the office, as he had been commanded by the King to attend the young Duke of Lennox in his travels on the Continent. His resignation was accepted, and on 21 January 1630 he announced his approaching departure to the Treasurer and Governors of St Bartholomew's Hospital, who thereupon appointed Dr Andrewes to deputize for him. About 23 December Harvey gave £100 towards the College of Physicians' Library site, and it was also in 1630 that Dr James Primrose, whom Haller styled 'contentiosus veterum defensor' and who presumably was hearing accounts of Harvey's discovery announced in his book of the previous year, published the first printed adverse account of it, which he called *Exercitationes et animadversiones in librum G. Harveii de Motu cordis*, and was dated from London. The Duke of Lennox went across to France about 28 July 1630 and soon after was probably met there by Harvey, but the exact details of the travels are not easy to trace.

In the following year Harvey became Physician to the King and to the Royal Household, and the King encouraged Physician's researches (though his own personal leanings were towards mathematics, according to Huxley, 1959, 167) and himself, with his nobles, used (Paget, 1846) to get Harvey to demonstrate his great discovery; monarch and subject must have constituted an advance Royal Society on their own.

Early in 1633 the King commanded Harvey to attend him on a journey to Scotland, the first he had made to his native country since his accession in 1625, and where his Scottish coronation was even then being planned. On the way to it a halt was made in Harvey's case at Worksop Manor, where he was entertained by the Earl of Arundel, while His Majesty stopped elsewhere. Edward Walker in *Historical Discourses*, said that 'Persons strived to outvie each other in the Bravery and Riches of their Apparel and Entertainment, but the

Earl kept his old Plainness, and yet wanted not the Honour and Esteem due to his Person and Quality.' Charles was duly crowned in the Abbey church at Holyrood, but in various tactless ways upset his northern subjects and thereby tended to make them 'Covenanters'. The City of Edinburgh, however, on 23 June gave a banquet for him, and Harvey for some reason was admitted a freeman and guild-holder. On 5 October he was back at Bart's as a physician without duties.

While in Edinburgh he had not shown any interest in court life or sectarian disputes, but to solve, if possible, certain problems about chick-formation within the egg, he had visited the Bass Rock, a landmark which he later described in Ex. 11 of *De generatione animalium* in the words: Est insula parva, Scoti Basse nominant . . . non procul a littore in alto mari sita, abrupto et confragoso clivo editissima (verius saxum ingens sive scopulum dixeris); haud amplius mille passuum circuitu amplitudo ejus clanditur. Hujus insulae superficies, mensibus Maio et junio, nidis, ovis, pullisque propemodum tota instrata est; adeo ut vix uspiam, prae corum copia, pedem libere ponere liceat: tantaque supervolitantium turba, ut, nubium instar, solem coelumque auferant; tantaque vociferantium clangor et strepitus, ut prope alloquentes vix audias. Which can be translated: 'There is a small island which the Scottish folk call the Bass Rock, lying in deep water, just off the shore. It is very distinct, with so broken and precipitous a slope that you could more properly speak of it as an enormous stone or a cliff; its circumference is almost completely covered with nests, eggs and fledglings so that it is impossible to step freely anywhere because of the number of them; and the swarm of those flying over is so great that they are like clouds blotting out the sun and the sky; and the clangour and din are so great that you can scarcely hear those talking nearby.'

After which breath of sea air one passes to the story of

73

the Lancashire witches, which began in the lying tale told by a boy in Pendle Forest in Lancashire in 1634. The child, in excuse for playing truant, accused a Mother Dickenson of being a witch and said she had seized him in her arms and ridden off with him with incredible swiftness over forests, fields, bogs and rivers until they came to a large barn, where she alighted, and taking him by the hand led him inside. There he saw seven old women pulling at seven halters which hung from the roof. As they pulled, large pieces of meat, lumps of butter, loaves of bread, basins of milk, hot puddings and black puddings fell from the halters on to the floor. Then a supper was provided, and when it was ready other witches came to share it. Many persons were arrested, for the boy was led from church to identify those he had seen in the barn. The report of this reached the ears of the King, who made arrangements for his Physician and the Royal Chirurgions to have the witches examined. The result was a pardon for four out of the seven convicted witches, 'which may have been due to the enlightened views and prompt and energetic action of Dr Harvey' (D'Arcy Power, 1897, 104).

Harvey's life as Court physician must have been a varied one, and on the birthday of her Serene Highness, Queen Henrietta Maria of Great Britain, France and Ireland, to wit, on 16 November 1635, His Majesty commanded him, with the help of the other Royal Physicians, to carry out an autopsy on one of his subjects, Thomas Parr, who had been a smallholder in the Shropshire village of Winnington up to the unbelievable age of an hundred and fifty-two years nine months, when the second Lord Arundel brought him from Shropshire to London and showed him to the King.

Harvey's notes on the autopsy remained in Latin manuscript until they were appended by John Bett, M.D., to his book entitled *De ortu et natura sanguinis*, London, 1669. According to Sir Geoffrey Keynes, their first English translation, by Robert Willis in the Sydenham Society's publications in 1847, was not satisfactory and this account is based on the one by Mr Arnold Muirhead, which appeared in *St Bart's Hosp. Rep.*, 1939, 72, 17–22. I am indebted to my old friend of post-war Oxford years for his permission to make use of his translation of this account of Parr, and it is a considerable pleasure to rest from translating oneself in this way.

Harvey's notes, so rendered, state, *inter alia*, that Parr's 'testes were large and sound and good enough not to give the lie to the story currently told of him that, after reaching his hundredth year, he was actually convicted of fornication and punished. Moreover, his wife, a widow whom he had married in his hundred-and-twentieth year, in reply to questions, could not deny that he had had intercourse with her exactly as other husbands do, and had kept up the practice to within twelve years of his death. . . . Until just before it, although he had been blind for twenty years, he could hear very well and understand what he heard, answer questions readily, and react normally to situations. He was even able to walk when lightly supported between two men. His power of memory [however] had failed considerably . . .'

'It was consistent to attribute the cause of death to a sudden adoption of a mode of living unnatural to him. Especially did he suffer harm from the change of air, for all his life he had enjoyed absolutely clean, rarefied, coolish and circulating air, and therefore his diaphragm and lungs could be inflated and deflated and refreshed more freely. But life in London in particular lacks this advantage—the more so because it is full of the filth of men, animals, canals and other forms of dirt, in addition to which there is the not inconsiderable grime from the smoke of sulphurous coal constantly used as fires. The air in London therefore is always heavy, and in autumn particularly so, especially to a man coming from the sunny and healthy district of Shropshire, and it could not but be particularly harmful to one who was now an enfeebled old man.

'Moreover he had always hitherto existed on one kind of diet and that of the simplest; therefore after he had gradually taken to a generous rich and varied diet, and stronger drink, he ruined the functions of almost all his natural parts. Finally, as the result of an increasingly sluggish stomach, less frequent expulsion of excreta, a slowing-up of the process of digestion, congestion of the liver, a less vigorous circulation of blood and numbness of his spirits, suppression of the activity of his heart which is the fount of life, constriction of the lungs which allowed no free passage of air, and the growing bulk of his body that prevented easy breathing and perspiration, it is not surprising that his soul was far from happy in such a prison and left it.

'. . . Even in his one hundred and thirtieth year in order to be able to earn a livelihood it was his custom to be vigorously engaged in some work on the land, and he even threshed wheat.'

In Venice in 1635 one Emilio Parisano (1567–1642) published *De cordis et sanguinis motu*, which was opposed to Harvey's views.

Towards 1636 King Charles I decided to send to Ratisbon an embassy of such weight and importance that a definite decision about the intentions of the Emperor with regard to the Palatinate could scarcely be withheld. Lord Arundel, whom we once again meet, was, according to Mrs Hervey (1921), the envoy selected for the mission, 'a desperate business indeed with no force to back it.' What reason, indeed, was there for hoping that, for mere words of persuasion, the Emperor, who was head of the Roman Catholic party, would restore to a Protestant prince the land and vote which he had just been successful in transferring to a Catholic, who was in addition his son-in-law. Arundel's duty to the King, and his affection for the Queen of Bohemia (Charles I's sister) and her family, led him to accept this difficult task and it is useful to picture him in words, as well as to visualize him as painted in the studio of Rubens. For it was his liking for Harvey which led to the latter's inclusion in the mission of 1636. 'The Earl was tall of Stature,' wrote Walker, 'and of shape and proportion rather goodly than neat; his Countenance was Majestic and grave, his Visage long, his Eyes large, black, and piercing, he had a hooked Nose, and some Wart or Moles on his Cheeks; his Countenance was broun, his Hair thin both on his Head and Beard; he was of a stately Presence and Gate, so that any Man who saw him, though in never so ordinary Habit, could not but conclude him to be a great Person, his Garb and Person drawing more observation than the rich Apparel of Others; so that it was a common Saying of the late Earl of Carlisle, Here comes the Earl of Arundel in his plain Stuff and trunk Hose, and his Beard in his Teeth, that looks more like a Noble Man than any of us.' Another description of him calls him 'the stately gentleman who went to Court sometimes because there only was a man greater than himself, and went there the seldomer because there was.' The Emperor mentioned in connection with the final stage of the Palatinate discussion was Ferdinand II.

The Embassy started from Greenwich by barge on Thursday, 7 April, dropped down river to Gravesend, took the coach thence to Canterbury with its boyhood recollections for Harvey, and spent the night there (D'Arcy Power, 1931). On Friday, 8 April, they left Canterbury for Margate in time for dinner, and at 3 p.m. embarked on the King's ship *The Happy Enterprise*. Saturday, 9 April, they spent at sea, landing at Helvoehts-sluis in Holland on Sunday, and going ashore without delay. They crossed the river at Maas-sluis and went on by wagon to Delft that afternoon; the Queen of Bohemia, whose husband had known Arundel in 1632, sent her carriages a mile out of town to welcome him, and the Embassy stayed at The Hague from Sunday, 10 April, to Thursday, 14 April, spending time on official visits. Harvey was held back by attendance on an indisposed member of the Embassy, and rejoined the main body in Köln on Thursday, 21 April. Lord Arundel visited the Jesuit College and Church on that day and was 'received with all civility'; he added, 'I found in the College honest little Doctor Harvey, who means to convert them.' The party stayed at Köln from Friday, 22 April, to Thursday, 28 April, when it was taken upstream, in a boat pulled by nine horses, past many plundered villages. The boat anchored the first night off Drachenfels and the party slept on board; the second night, Friday, they anchored off Andernach. On Saturday the boat was shelled as it passed Boppard and on Whit Sunday they continued on past Baccharach, 'where the poor people are found dead with grass in their mouths' because they are starving, to Assmanshausen, and on Whit Monday to Mainz, where they anchored. 'Heere likewise the poore people were almost starved . . . and after supper some of them strove so violently' at the sight of relief sent from the Ship 'that some of them fell into the Rhine and were like to have bin drowned.' 'The whole journey so far was hazardous, for active hostilities were in progress.' 'From Collein [Köln] hither all the Townes, Villages and Castles bee battered, pillaged, or burnt, and every place we lay at on the Rhine on shipboard we watched taking every man his turne.'

The Main was reached on Thursday, 3 May, and Frankfurt on the same day, the danger from freebooters being a very realized one. Hollar, the engraver, probably referred to this stretch when he told Aubrey (1813, 2, 384) that 'Dr Harvey would still be making observations of strange trees and plants, earths, etc., and sometimes he was like to be lost, so that my Lord Ambassador would be really angry

78

with him for there was not only a danger of thieves but also of wild beasts.'

The party rested at Frankfurt from 3 to 8 May, and one hopes that Harvey called on William Fitzer and had good news of *De motu cordis et sanguinis in animalibus*. They then went onwards towards Würzburg, which they reached on Monday, 9 May, and Nuremburg, not far from which was the University of Altdorf, where one who had been a Paduan fellow-student with Harvey was Professor of Medicine. This was Caspar Hofmann (1572–73 November 1648), who had spiritedly and sustainedly rejected Galen's intra-septal pores, had assumed that arterial blood is driven into veins through anastomoses, and had stated that in the embryo the heart forms two vessels—the artery and the vein—through which 'the blood goes and returns'.

More remarkable is the fact commented on by Baier in 1728 and again by Richard Landau in 1902, but apparently overlooked thereafter, that in April 1622 the idea of a circulation of the blood had been proposed to Hofmann by his own pupil Helvicus Dieterich (1601–55). The occasion was a public disputation at which Dieterich was defending a thesis on the function of the brain. His own account of how his proposition was received indicates Hofmann's attitude so clearly that it is worth quoting in full:

'Moreover,' he said, 'I there dissected several animals, both living and dead, and in more than one vivisection of a dog I carried out, as physicians still living will testify, almost the identical experiment by which, not long afterwards, the learned Harvey taught the whole medical world the movement and circulation of the blood. Then, like Terence's young Phaedra, I was overwhelmed with delight and immediately announced the new discovery which had been revealed to me to my teacher, Master Hofmann, really persuading myself that surely the motion of the blood could hardly be other than circular. From him, however, I had for answer only his customary "Pah", together with his wise-crack, "You don't want to become a circulator, do you?" '

It is not improbable that rumours of Harvey's lectures at the College of Physicians in London had already been discussed on the Continent. The fact that letters (now lost) which had passed between Harvey and Hofmann were cited to refute those who denied Harvey's priority leads one to believe that Hofmann had heard something of the circulation direct from Harvey, and that he had thus early come to an adverse opinion of it, an opinion vividly reflected in this passage from his pupil's book.

One of the most interesting new facts revealed in Harvey's just published (1960) new letter to Hofmann is his statement that there were English anatomists who did not publicly hesitate to say that he, Harvey, had taken his ideas of the circulation from Hofmann and he had had to produce his letters and to show the dates in order to refute the charges. According to D'Arcy Power (1917, 148), the demonstration of the circulation offered by Harvey at Altdorf was said to have been given in public and to have proved satisfactory to everyone except Hofmann himself. As he remained unconvinced and continued to urge objections, Harvey at length threw down his knife and walked out of the theatre.

The party went on, but Harvey left it at Augsburg and went to see Lord Feilding at Venice and to execute a commission for the King, running into some customs difficulty on the way. On the return journey the party visited Köln, Düsseldorff, Utrecht, and Leijden, where the University and the Anatomy School were found of interest. After dinner they went to The Hague, leaving later for Rotterdam. 'At 11 of the clocke in the night took boates and went to our ship called the Garland and about 3 in the afternoone set sayle and sayled over the barre, having a Pilot sayling before us with a lanthorne on the top of his mast sounding for the depth all the way. And the next day at twelve of the clocke

Merton College, Oxford; from an eighteenth-century print.

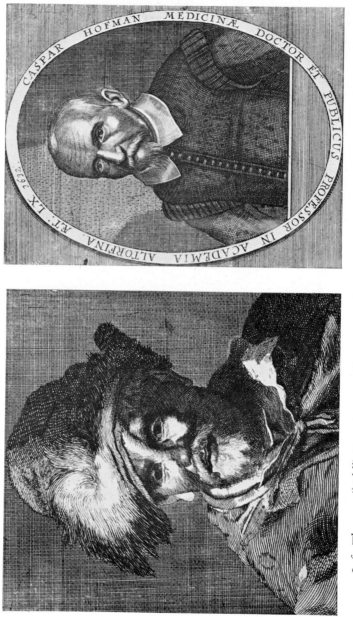

Left: Thomas ('Old') Parr; from an old print. *Right:* Caspar Hofmann; from Boissard's *Bibliotheca chalcographia* (1650)

Caption on portrait: CASPAR HOFMAN MEDICINÆ DOCTOR ET PUBLICUS PROFESSOR IN ACADEMIA ALTORFINA ÆT. LX. 1632.

cast anchor in the Downs and there rode and could not land for the roughness of the sea until Tuesday morning the 27th December and then landed at Deale and thence by poast to Canterbury and so to Sittingbourne to bed. The next day in the morning early to Gravesend and then took water to London.'

There is one further thing that needs to be done in respect of the story of 1636 and that is to listen in imagination to Harvey discoursing mellifluously in his seventeenth-century English. To get an idea of this one can quote one of the 'Eleven Letters of William Harvey to Lord Feilding', which were purchased from the Earl of Denbigh and presented to the College of Physicians by Sir Thomas Barlow, Bt., President, on 18 October 1912.

The first letter is headed 'Lintz' and reads:

'Righthon^{ble}.

My Sweete Lord: soe much the more I now condemn my self (having att this hower receyved such sweete and loving lines from you) in that I did not send those letters I intended by the bearer hereof, his suddayne and unexpected departure was the cause that from Nuremburg I did not present my humble service which I beseech you to accept in excuse, and not lay on me soe fowle a fault as neglect of one soe extreamely well desearving, and to me ever soe kind and frendly. I thank your Honor that you vouchsafe to advertise me of one, whome I hard before would wryte against me, but till now never heard he did, or ever yett saw that Book; we are heare lately arrived thorowgh that ruined desolat country of Germany into Austria and att Lintz have had only twise audience, our bysenss, to expect the delivery of the palatinate, is not unknown to your Eccl^y. My lord will omitt noe dilligens or labour to effect it, this day sum of us accompanyed his M^{tey} the Emperor a-hunting, . . . Yf ever I have done and may be able to doe service to you ther is nothing wilbe more comfort and joy unto me, wheare all good endeavours bring forth much good frute and all service is soe plentifully acknowledged.

I should be glad of any occasion to see venis [Venice], once more soe much the rather to have the happiness of your conversation untill which time I will live in hope to see your Eccl^y and in certenty ever to remayne

Your Eccel. lordships
Humble att Command
Will. Harvey'

D'Arcy Power (1931, 171) summarized the whole year very succinctly when he wrote, 'The fact that Harvey at the age of 58 undertook a journey through a country desolated by war shows that he was of an enterprising spirit [but was he not commanded by King Charles I?—K.J.F.], and loved travel,' whilst the little aside in his second letter from Linz that 'we drunke hard' tends to show that perhaps his gout was acquired and not inherited, for it must have needed some previous training to have enabled him to hold his own at a seventeenth-century Kneipe.

On 13 February 1637 he was at a meeting of the College of Physicians, and early in summer 1639 he went with the King and Lord Arundel, who by a change in standing was now commander of a large army, to Scotland. But the troops sided with the Scottish and the King on 18 June signed the so-called 'Pacification of Berwick' and returned to London. Dr Bethune, who was the senior Royal Physician-in-Ordinary, died in July and Harvey was appointed in his place, the appointment carrying with it a lodging in Whitehall and certain other perquisites.

The influential Professor of Leijden, Franciscus Sylvius (1614–72), accepted the Harveian idea of the circulation in his lectures of 1639 (see *Disputationes medicae*, 1663, Amsterdam) and in 1640 his pupil, J. Walaeus or J. van Wale (1604–49) published his *De motu chyli et sanguinis* ad Thomam Bartholinum, Casp. Filium, on p. 254 of which he wrote in the following words about a contractility which he had seen in the vena cava:

'Pelli autem *a vena cava* sanguinem in *dextram cordis auriculam*, manifesto in vivis dissectis animalibus conspeximus: in omni enim cordis motu a vena cava primu[m] initium est, quod cum dubitaremus an non fieret, quia cava auriculae cordique connexa esset, cor & auriculam resecuimus prorsus in canibus vivis à vena cava, & animadvertimus etiam tum venam cavam pulsare minimum, & singulis vicibus aliquid sanguinis effundere. Quare & plerumque circa cor vena cava carneas quasdam fibras accepit, quas alibi in vena cava haud invenias: eae admodum conspicuae in hominis, bovis, canis cava possunt videri. Motus autem ille venae cavae prope cor evidentissimus est, ut plurimum tamen eum quoque in vivis canibus observavimus toto illo ductu ab hepate & a jugulo in cor usque.'

This may be translated: 'In dissections of living animals I have clearly seen the blood driven from the vena cava to the right auricle of the heart: for in every heart movement the first beginning of the movement is from the vena cava. As I doubted whether it was not happening because the vena cava was connected to the auricle and the heart, I at once cut away from the vena cava in living dogs [both] the heart and the auricle, and noticed that even in those conditions the vena cava still pulsated a very little and in individual beats discharged some blood. For this reason, especially near the heart, you may find the cava endowed with certain fleshy fibres, such as you may not find elsewhere in that vessel; those fibres are rather visible in the venae cavae of man, the ox, and the dog. Moreover, that movement of the vena cava is extremely apparent near the heart so that I have seen it in the whole of that channel from the liver and neck right on to the heart.'

On receiving Dr L. Chauvois's review of my translation, etc., of *Exercitationes duae anatomicae de circulatione sanguinis*, I found that he attached far more importance than did I to a difference which he had skilfully noticed between Harvey's *Exercitationes* of 1628 and 1649 respectively, and which he had linked up with his *Place aux veines* of 1951.

For my own part, I am happy if Harvey's new idea of the circulation is combined in thought with the work of Allison (1839) and others, including Jan van Wale (1640). Nor am I unduly concerned that this last was not referred to by Harvey, though he could have known of it, for from 1631, when he became physician to King Charles I and to the Royal Household (Paget, 1846), the greater part of his time was spent at Court and he had many calls upon his time and energies.

The contraction of the veins which enter into the auricles was Allison's main subject of interest and research, and a century later, in 1938, Champy and Louvel wrote of *La contraction de la veine cave supérieure*, and also filmed the rapid systolo-diastolic contraction of the terminal portion of this vessel which occurred in an experimental animal. I have myself seen it sufficiently often in such subjects, but cannot off-hand recall having seen it in cineradiographic records of unoperated ones, though I should not be surprised so to do. In 1951 in his *Place aux veines*, Dr Chauvois indicated the 'rôle initial et primordial du secteur veineux dans le circuit sanguin' and referred to a review of *Veines* by J. J. Louvel and J. J. Laubry in 1950. Senac in 1749 had written about the idea which existed long before that of a fermentation of the blood, and stated that 'On n'observe point que le sang bouillonne en sortant du coeur, il n'occupe plus d'éspace que le sang artérial; dans les artères mêmes il n'est pas plus rarefié que dans les veines'. The same author (p. 230) said that the heart's activity is innate, but that the skeletal muscles support its activity by their tonic movement acting upon the veins, an idea which was re-expressed by Yandell Henderson *et al.* in 1934 in their note about 'the third major mechanical factor in the circulation of the blood'.

But we must return to the seventeenth century and to Harvey. 'Many,' wrote Herringham in 1928, 'must have wondered why the College of Physicians never elected as its President the first Englishman who was definitely what we now mean as a scientific man. Well,' said the writer, 'it is not hard to see why. At that time political animosity had reached its height. Charles had received the Grand Remonstrance from the Commons, and in that very year made the attempt to seize the five members, which caused the Commons to adjourn from Westminster to the City under the pretext that they were in need of protection. . . . Is it to be wondered at that the College, meeting at the very foot of the great cathedral round which the City clusters, should feel as the City felt, and that the majority would not, and the minority dared not, elect as their head one who, though no politician, was yet of the Royal Household, and closely attached to the Royal person?

'When he came back many years later his King was a captive, and soon afterwards executed, the Royalists were broken and dispersed, his collections and his notes, the labour of many years, had been destroyed by the mob which sacked his house, and again can we wonder that when, after his munificent gift of a Library,[1] the College offered him its Chair, the old man with kindly courtesy declined it, and chose, not among the cares and pomp of office, but in the affectionate conversation of his family, in reading and in

[1] The Library was unfinished when Harvey made his will, for he left money to complete it.

meditation, to pass the tranquil sunset of his busy and honourable day?'

Thomas Hobbes of Malmesbury, who was a friend of Harvey and who in 1647 was to become tutor to the Prince of Wales, afterwards Charles II, wrote in his book *Behemoth*, 'the history of the causes of the Civil Wars of England, and of the counsels and artifices by which they were carried on from the year 1640 to the year 1660.' 'In the year 1640,' he said, 'the government of England was monarchical, and the King that reigned, Charles, the first of that name, holding the sovereignty, by right of a descent continued above six hundred years, and from a much longer descent King of Scotland, and from the time of his ancestor Henry II, King of Ireland; a man that wanted no virtue, either of body or mind, nor endeavoured anything more than to discharge his duty towards God, in the well governing of his subjects.'

On the other hand, 'the city of London and other great towns of trade, having in admiration the prosperity of the Low Countries after they had revolted from their monarch, the King of Spain, were inclined to think that the like change of government here, would to them produce the like prosperity.'

Hobbes then referred to 'the fortune of one day; in which, at Naseby, the King's army was utterly overthrown, and no hope left him to raise another. Therefore after the battle he went up and down, doing the Parliament here and there some shrewd turns, but never much increasing his number.' He also spoke of Fairfax ... 'forcing my Lord Hopton upon honourable terms to disband his army, and with the Prince of Wales to pass over to Scilly; whence not long after they went to Paris.'

There followed the capture and confinement of the King, his trial and sentence of death 'and the same upon Tuesday after, January 30th 1649, executed at the gate of his own palace of Whitehall'. In the chronicle the reader 'shall see what courage, patience, wisdom, and goodness was in this prince, whom in their charge the members of that wicked Parliament styled tyrant, traitor, and murderer.'

Herringham (1929, 30–32) said, 'It has been claimed that the Puritans preserved the family life of England from the corruption and the licentiousness of Court manners. Such statements assume, on the one hand, that the Court society of the day was something exceptional, and, on the other hand, that the manners of the Capital were the manners of the country. Neither is true. . . .'

'It is said, too, that to the Puritans we owe that sturdiness which has kept and increased the liberty they won. Neither is this to be accepted. Lived there no brave men before Agamemnon? . . .

'The temper of a great nation is a thing too firmly set to change under every blast of new doctrine, and its history is the consequence of its character, not the cause of it.'

'The Puritans were the guardians of spiritual fervour at a season when religion had become cold and dead. Such seasons of decay occur from time to time, and the Puritans are neither the first nor the last of the Revivalists. Whenever need arises, such men have a great part cast for them on the world's theatre, and none of us should criticize them so hardly as to refuse them their due praise.'

'But we owe to them the loss of half the beauty of England. They destroyed the drama, they sold the finest collection of pictures in Europe, and even ordered the religious pictures to be burnt as superstitious; there is not a village church which does not bear the marks of their barbarous hands, and three several times it was proposed in Parliament to pull down the Cathedrals and sell the materials for what they would fetch.'

'But, after all, our interest is not to praise the actors in this great tragedy. It is to consider what was Harvey's attitude to the great struggles, political and religious, that were taking place round him. And of this we obtain from himself no evidence whatever. He mentions the King and Queen two or three times in *De Generatione*, but without any word of special affection or regret, which indeed in 1651 it might not have been prudent to print. He mentions Parliament once, complaining that as he was attending the King with their permission and even at their command they might have prevented the mob from destroying his collections. There remains only the message that he is said to have sent to Scarburgh, who was an ardent Royalist, "Leave thy gunning and come here and I will bring thee into practice."

'We may well believe that he would not approve either the folly and tyranny of Charles, of which he must have known from his brothers, or the violence and malice of his foes. To Harvey the war must have seemed a vast catastrophe for which both parties were alike responsible, from which little good was likely to be gained, and which was destructive of the one thing he cared about, the advance of knowledge.

'And for religion. Few men of serious character then doubted the fundamental beliefs of Christianity, and Harvey was of a reverent mind. But we cannot fancy him sympathizing either with Laud's extreme love of ceremony or with the brutal irreverence of the Puritans. Harvey's religious findings, we may be sure, were too sincere and too deeply felt ever to be published to the world.'

The King's Proclamation, dated 9 August 1642, from the Court at York was read, so far as Oxford is concerned, by the Public Magistrate on 13 August; it denounced the Earl of Essex as a traitor (Varley, 1932). Nine days thereafter the King set up his standard at Nottingham, and summoned the gentry of the north and for twenty miles south of the Trent to meet him there (Varley, 1932). According to Belloc (1936) the setting up of the standard took place in a big field south of the town, and the King had about him as yet no more than 2,000 men. 'The gale was from the north and that night his flag was blown down: an omen.' Harvey had left London with the King on 16 August and later wrote (*De generatione animalium*, 502), 'And, while I deal with these matters, let untroubled minds forgive me if, with recollections of my extreme losses, I give vent to a slight sigh. My cause of sorrow is that, when I was in attendance upon our most serene King during our late troubles and more than civil wars, not only by the leave but at the order of Parliament, some grasping hands not only pillaged all my household furniture but also—a more serious cause of regret to me—upset in my study my files resulting from many years of work. This resulted in the destruction of numerous observations, particularly on the generation of insects, with loss—if I may be permitted to say so, to the literature on the subject.'

It was, one imagines, from Nottingham that Harvey called on his friend Percival Willoughby, who had been admitted an extra-licentiate of the College of Physicians on 20 February 1640. They discussed several infirmities incident to the womb and after Willoughby 'had related the aforegoing story *de caudâ mulieris*, and how she flouded, and was cured,' Harvey added to Willoughby's knowledge an infirmity, 'which he had seen in women, & hee gave it the name of a honeycomb, which also, hee said would cause flouding in women.' According to Spencer (1921), it is interesting that Harvey was able to add to the knowledge of an experienced gynaecologist information about a previously undescribed disease, the 'honeycombe', which was presumably an epithelioma.

It is also of interest that he could turn his mind off to gynaecology when so near the outbreak of the first major conflict of the Civil War. This was the battle of Edgehill, which took place indecisively on 23 October 1642. Harvey was present not far from the fighting, and the traditional story is that the Prince of Wales and his brother, the Duke of York, were entrusted to his care (Aubrey, 1813, 2, 379). 'He told me,' wrote Aubrey, 'that he withdrew with them under a hedge, and tooke out of his pockett a booke and read; but he had not read very long before a bullet of a great gun grazed on the ground neare him, which made him remove his station.' Sir Arthur MacNalty and Sir Geoffrey Keynes, according to the former, incline to the view that the oil-painting of the Princes, which the King later gave to Harvey and which was painted by William Dobson (1610–46), commemorated the Prince of Wales's baptism by fire at Edgehill, but Dr D. Stewart and also, it appears, the Editor of the *British Medical Journal*, thought that that story was apocryphal, and Dr Stewart tells me that, as no one wrote about his note which he sent to the *Journal*, he presumes that no one had any evidence to submit contrary to the views which he had put forward.

At Edgehill Sir Jacob Astley, a veteran of much experience whom King Charles I appointed Major-General in his army and who was the first governor of Oxford appointed by his Majesty, is remembered for his soldier's prayer and exhortation, 'O Lord, Thou knowest how busy I must be this day: if I forget Thee, do not Thou forget me. March on, boys!' (Varley, 1932, 70; Wedgwood, 1959, 136).

Aubrey continued with his story of Harvey at Edgehill: 'he told me yt Sir Adrian Scrope was dangerously wounded there, and left for dead among the dead men, stript; which happened to be the saving of his life. It was cold, clear weather, and a frost that night; which staunched his bleeding, and about midnight, or some hours after his hurt, he awaked, and was faine to drawe a dead body upon him for warmeth sake.' Anthony Wood also spoke of this, saying: 'This most valiant person, who was son of Sir Jervais Scrope, did most loyally attend his Majesty at the fight of Edgehill, where receiving several wounds he was stripped and left among the dead, as a dead person there, but brought off by his son and recovered by the immortal Dr Will. Harvey, who was there but withdrawn under a hedge with the Prince and the Duke while the battle was at its height.'

When the battle began in earnest, the King, in a black velvet cloak lined with ermine, rode along his troops encouraging them, and he also exhorted the leading officers in his tent, saying that he was the Royalists' cause, their quarrel and their captain and that, come life or death, he would bear them company and gratefully remember their service at Edgehill that day. A spectacular incident was the recovery of the Royal Standard, carried by Sir Edmund Verney at the beginning of the fight and retrieved after his death by a Captain John Smith, who as Sir John was mortally wounded at Alresford in 1644.

Had Edgehill been a victory for the Royalists, the King could have moved south and east and have had a good chance of a decisive action against London, as Prince Rupert had suggested. Instead, his army moved on to Banbury and Oxford at no great pace, and he made a state entry into the city of Oxford with the Princes Charles and James, his sons, and the Princes Rupert and Maurice, his nephews, on 29 October. After that date Harvey more or less settled down to scientific academic pursuits for nearly four years, incorporating as Doctor of Medicine of Oxford on 7 December 1642, the year in which Nathanael Highmore (1631–85) proceeded to the degree in the normal way. Later, Highmore dedicated to Harvey ('amico suo singulari') his *Corporis humani disquisitio anatomica*, 1651, the first text-book of anatomy produced in this country in which the circulation was fully recognized. Thomas Willis (1621–75), who was at Christ Church from 1636, took the degree of M.A. in June 1642 and 'about then bore arms for the King', after which he read and practised medicine, and resided in Beam Hall, Oxford, opposite Merton College, where Queen Henrietta

Maria (with her court) had her lodging from 14 July 1643 until her departure from Oxford on 17 April 1644, occupying the room which was still known in 1897 as 'the Queen's room', together with the drawing-room next to it. Later Willis went to London, where he became for a while the leading physician; he was also to become one of the first Fellows of the Royal Society. Another interesting figure in the Oxford story was Walter Charleton (1619–95) who, though only 22 on the retirement of the King to Oxford, was created Doctor of Medicine and then Physician to his Majesty. He, too, became one of the original Fellows of the Royal Society. Charles Scarburgh (1615–93), who with the Civil War was ejected from his Fellowship at Gonville and Caius College, Cambridge, withdrew to Oxford and entered himself at Merton, where he became a friend of Harvey and helped him considerably in his studies of the generation of animals. Harvey gave Scarburgh letters testimonial for incorporating as Doctor of Medicine of Oxford on 23 June 1646, and the two men remained firm friends up to Harvey's death (Payne, L.M., 1957). Harvey also worked in Trinity College on generation in chickens; unfortunately, Ralph Bathurst, the man with whom he worked, was killed in defending Faringdon in 1644.

It may well be asked what was the reaction of Oxford to the advent of soldiery into the City, and it can be left to F. J. Varley to provide the answer, which begins: 'There can be little doubt that the great majority of the citizens or townsmen throughout the period of the Royalist occupation of Oxford was strongly anti-Royalist. But from 4 November 1642, when the King took the precaution of disarming the town, the citizens had little opportunity of any overt demonstration in favour of the Rebels, and they probably resigned themselves to the inevitable. According to Wood, many of them waxed rich in supplying the wants of the Court and garrison of Oxford, and doubtless there was, in spite of military orders, plenty of opportunity for profiteering. . . .

'With the entry of the King and the bulk of his army after the Battle of Edgehill, the citizens had to submit to the inevitable with as good grace as possible, and to meet the King with protestations of loyalty, which he knew well were feigned. There was a general disarming of the citizens on 4 November, when muskets and powder were taken away from the Guildhall and lodged in the uppermost room of the Schools Tower, but on 15 December the King ordered the City to bring in more arms, as the citizens had doubtless succeeded in evading the general order.'

On 1 and 2 November 1642 degrees were conferred by Oxford University on Prince Charles, the Duke of York and others, and in late December Parliament in London sent Commissioners to King Charles in Oxford to treat about a peace, though on 14 April 1643 the Treaty ended ineffectively. According to Herringham (1928, 6), the House of Commons resolved in that year that Harvey, as a follower of the King, should be dismissed from his position at St Bartholomew's Hospital, and as a result, after thirty-six years of service, his connexion with the Hospital ended, and the entry stood in its usual place for the last time to say 'Itm to Doctor Harvey Phisicon xxxiii^l vi^s viii^d'. On 17 October he reported, with Edmund Smith and others, on the health of Prince Maurice at a time when 'morbus campestris' (the ordinary raging disease of the army, a slow fever with great dejection of strength) was rife. The patient showed a humble, thankful sense when Harvey expressed his Majesty's sorrow and great care for him, and he was successfully treated by a small amount of medicine and a regular diet. In October 1643 Reading was occupied by the Royalists, and in January 1644 members of both houses of the Oxford Parliament assembled in the Hall of Christ Church, where the King made a speech to them. In April he accompanied the Queen to Abingdon, where he spent the night, and he came back after parting from her (neither of them knowing that it was to be for the last time). She continued her journey westward via Lambourn and Bristol by easy stages to Exeter, where Sir Theodore de Mayerne and Sir Matthew Lister attended her, and where she gave birth to a daughter, Elizabeth. After that, as Exeter was in danger of a siege, she went off from Plymouth Sound in a Dutch boat to France, all this being as courageously carried out as her raising of money and buying of munitions and guns for the King had been in 1643.

At this point I propose to interpolate an account of King Charles's famous night ride of 3 June 1644. It is reproduced by very kind permission of Messrs. Macmillan & Co. Ltd., of St Martin's Street, London, W.C.2, and is taken from pp. 39–40 of *Highways and Byways in Oxford and the Cotswolds*, 1916, which was written by the late Professor Herbert A. Evans, of Yarnton, Oxon., the village where it is my present good fortune to live. Having recently tried to get through from either end the electrified fencing and brambles and so on of Frogwelldown Lane, I can state that the green track now known by that name must have been much more passable in 1644.

'Although,' wrote Professor Evans, 'no events of national import have given Yarnton a place in the pages of history, the night of June 3rd, 1644, must have been long remembered by the villagers. It was on this night that the King at the head of 3,000 horse and 2,500 foot made his memorable dash from Oxford between the two armies destined by the Parliament to complete the circumvallation of the city—the army of Essex on his right, and that of Waller on his left. The former had passed the Cherwell and had already pushed as far westwards as Woodstock and Kidlington, while the latter lay on the left bank of the Thames round about Stanton Harcourt and Eynsham. A few more hours and the two commanders would have joined hands, Oxford would have been completely surrounded, and a single fortnight have sufficed to compel it to surrender. This catastrophe was only prevented by the spirited resolution and prompt action of the King; the enterprise was a hazardous one, and he could not hope to succeed in it without the utmost caution and secrecy. His object was to secure the passage of the Evenlode at Handborough bridge, a point about midway between the hostile armies, before either of their generals had any suspicion that he had quitted Oxford. It was therefore an imperative necessity to keep out of sight and hearing of the enemy, and this he could not do if he took the ordinary high road to the bridge across the open plain of Campsfield; here, in spite of the darkness, his advance would inevitably be detected by Essex's scouts, and a flank attack would bring up Waller from the other side, and the two armies would crush the Royalists between them. Charles therefore chose the lower road, where the rising ground on his right would conceal his movements, and by means of which under the cover of night he might hope to reach the bridge unperceived. It was this lower road which brought him through Yarnton. The changes in the water level brought about by the Thames Navigation Act have since rendered it impracticable, but in those days it was the shortest way from Oxford to Yarnton and Handborough, and was the one commonly used by the market people of both villages. From Oxford it led across Portmeadow to Lower Wolvercot, and thence across the meadows quaintly called Pixey and Oxey, where as each summer comes round the Yarnton farmers still draw lots for the several portions of mowing grass, past the manor house and church till it reached the mouth of a wide green lane, which then ran through an unenclosed country in a straight line to the Evenlode bridge. About a mile of this green track, now known as Frogwelldown lane, still remains to remind the traveller of the dawn of the June morning over three centuries ago when King

Charles and his troopers passed along it. By this skilful manœuvre the great scheme of the Parliament was frustrated, and for the rest of the year, as far as the south of England was concerned, the tide of success was turned in favour of the Royalists. The King had crossed the Evenlode and halted his army on Northleigh heath before any intelligence of his successful sortie reached either Waller or Essex, and he had made good his way as far as Burford before any of their cavalry came up with him.'

On 27 January 1645 the King, at that time lodged in Christ Church, sent letters stating that Sir Nathaniel Brent, the Warden of Merton College, had been away for nearly three years, and had adhered to the Rebels and accepted the office of Judge Marshal among them—he could also have added that Brent had actually signed the Covenant. The King's letters accordingly pronounced Brent as desposed, and directed the seven senior Fellows to present three eligible successors from whom his Majesty would choose one. Five of these senior Fellows, including the Sub-Warden, placed Harvey first upon their lists, and the King straightway nominated him as Warden, a post which he assumed on 9 April 1645. Two days later, according to the Register of the College, the new Warden addressed a Fellows' Meeting in Hall, saying that his predecessors in that office had perhaps gone after the Wardenship for their pecuniary advantage but he with altogether different intent, namely, that the *College* [my italics—K.J.F.] might rather gain and profit thereby: at the same time he carefully and diligently exhorted the Fellows to foster agreement and amity between themselves (Andrew, 1890, 6–7).

In the *Miscellaneous works of John Greaves*, ed. Birch, 1757, there is an account of a conversation of Sir John Greaves, Fellow of the College, Savilian Professor of Astronomy and senior Linacre lecturer on Anatomy, with Harvey which is well worthy of a reference here as showing the latter's comprehensive outlook and perspicacity. It says: 'That I and my company should have continued so many hours in the Pyramid and live (whereat we found no inconvenience) was much wondered at by Dr Harvey, his majesty's learned physician. For, said he, seeing we never breathe the same air twice, but still new air is required to a new respiration (the succus olibilis of it being spent in every expiration), it could not be but by long breathing we should have spent the aliment of that small stock of air within, and have been stifled; unless there were some secret tunnel conveying it to the top of the Pyramid whereby it might pass out and make way for fresh air to come in at the entrance below.' The Fellow of Merton was not wanting in an answer to the future Warden, assuring him, amongst much else not wholly correct, that 'as for any tubuli to let out the fuliginous air at the top of the Pyramid none could be discovered within or without'. Harvey replied, 'they might be so small as that they could not easily be discerned, and yet might be sufficient to make way for the air, being a thin and subtil body.'

It has, indeed, been left to our own times and to V. Pettenkofer to demonstrate and exhibit the action of the capillary pores in the constituents of a mass of 'solid' masonry (see his Dezie hungen der Luft zu Kleidung, Wohnung und Boden, 1872, pp. 41–45, and especially the figures on p. 42). What Leeuwenhoek and Malpighi did for the capillaries of the human body in supplementation of Harvey's work, and in correction of one of his few errors, that V. Pettenkofer has done in supplementation of Harvey's suggestion as to 'tubuli so small as that they could not be discerned' in something like the Pryamids. It is, perhaps, not more than curious to note that Harvey was equally right in suggesting the existence of larger 'secret tunnels': an account of the discovery and opening of these may be found in Colonel Howard Vyse's Operations carried on at the Pyramids of Gizeh, 1837, i, pp. 3, 263, 285–88, ii, pp. 160, 161; and an amusing history of the inconveniences endured in the interior of the Pyramids previously to the discovery of these 'air-channels' is given by Colonel Coutelle in *Description de l'Egypte, Antiquités, Mémoires*, ii, p. 46, 1809.

The King remained in Oxford in winter quarters from 5 November 1645 up to the time of his flight (Varley, 1932, 131). The only hope of enabling the Royalists to take the field in the spring seemed to the Council in Oxford to be in collecting a force from the few garrisons left, and from Wales. On this mission Lord Astley was sent to Worcester, but on his way back was caught on 21 March 1645–46, at Stow-on-the-Wold by the Rebels under Sir W. Brereton, and he and his officers were taken prisoners.

A letter dated 27 April from Colonel Payne, Commander of the garrison at Abingdon, reports intelligence that the King went disguised to London and made use of Sir Thomas Fairfax's seal 'which they have gotten cut in Oxford'; another letter dated 29 April gives a circumstantial account of the flight:

'News is confirmed by all that come from Oxford that he went out disguised in a Montero with a hat upon it. Sir Thomas Glenham, the Governor of Oxford, at his parting bade him "Farewell Harry" by which name, it seems, he goes.' He was accompanied by the Earl of Southampton, Dr King and Mr Ashburnham, described as 'the closest of his friends' (Belloc, 1936, 302).

Paget (1846, 43) wrote about Harvey that he returned to London: but I can find no indication that he ever again took interest in the affairs of the hospital; although while he lived so near it (in the Poultry, with his brother Sir Eliab), and the College of Physicians, where he must have passed much time, was much closer at hand, it can hardly be doubted that he often visited the scene of his former labours, and watched the working of his Code of rules.

In November, according to Herringham, (1929, 5) he was

given a pass by Parliament from Oxford to Newcastle to attend the King as his physician. But he did not follow the King to Holmby House, nor do we find that he was ever again in attendance.

F. J. Varley (personal communication) wrote to me on 7 April 1948 that 'Harvey was certainly in residence at the surrender of Oxford in June 1646 and left on a passport under the Articles of Surrender for London, where he resided with his brothers. I cannot find that he was ever in trouble with the Commonwealth or Protectorate authorities, nor did he suffer any sequestration.' But David Lloyd, in his undated 'Memorials of certain persons who suffered during the Rebellion', stated, I hear, that Harvey was fined £2,000 by Parliament. The rest of his life was devoted to the College of Physicians. Sir Nathaniel Brent returned as Warden without opposition, and the Visitation of Oxford followed.

C. G. Paget (1929, 28) wrote that, with the close of the struggle between King and Parliament in 1646, a new situation had become apparent, namely, the increased power of the Army, nominally under the leadership of Sir Thomas Fairfax, but in fact organized and inspired by Oliver Cromwell, and with different aims and views from those held by Parliament as a whole. This latter body in fact made an attempt early in 1647 to disband the Army, and the country as a whole became restive under the unaccustomed domination, with the result that a strong feeling for the reinstatement of the King arose. Thus in April 1648 there was an uprising of the apprentices of London in his favour and it had to be forcibly suppressed, while in May the men of Surrey gave a striking example of the reversion of feeling towards the sovereign which occurred at that time, and in July forces were sent to Croydon, Epsom and Ewell 'to prevent those places from tumultuating'. Towards the end of 1648 the independent party determined to get rid of the

King and, as the project would obviously not be successfully carried through Parliament, they resorted on 6 December to the strange expedient which came to be known as 'Pride's Purge', and which resulted in the imprisonment of forty-seven members and the exclusion of ninety-six. The Parliament, expurgated in such fashion and derisively known as 'The Rump', ordained a commission to try the King. The 'trial' took place on 20 January 1649 when the King, who refused to plead before this illegally constituted tribunal, was condemned to death. He went to his end in Whitehall on 30 January, says Paget, 'with a dignity and courage which did much to wipe away the remembrance of his political sins'.

According to Salter (1956, 71) the Reverend Hugh Peters (1598–1660) 'reputed to have been one of the two executioners of King Charles I, was a strong Puritan and was appointed to a lectureship at St Sepulchre's in 1630'. Of these lectures he tells us that 'the resort grew so great that it caused envy and anger, though a hundred every week were persuaded from sin to Christ'. When London became too hot for him he went to Holland, and became Pastor of the English Church in Rotterdam. He emigrated to New England in 1635 and, as Army Chaplain, exercised great influence in the Roundheads. He was given rooms in Whitehall Palace by Cromwell, and 'Parliament made over to him Laud's library after the latter's execution' (10 January 1645). Hugh Peters was himself executed at Charing Cross and met his doom with fortitude and 'in the sure hope of a glorious resurrection'. According to an imaginary account in the *Chest and Heart Bulletin*, when Charles the First was executed in Whitehall, 'blood gushed in a fountain several feet high from the headless body. . . . Such is the ability of the elastic arteries to transmit, at a distance, the power of the cardiac beat.' It is strange indeed that Harvey, who only twenty-one years earlier had dedicated his new account of the heart to the most Serene and most Puissant Charles, had called him 'the new splendour of this age, and indeed its whole heart, its central figure abounding in virtue and grace, [to whom] we rightly refer whatever good obtains in this England of ours, whatever pleasure in our life within it.' It is sad to read (Herringham, 1929, 5) that in September 1648 the King had asked that Harvey or Dr Wetherbourne, his physicians, and Humphrey Painter, his surgeon, might be sent to him at Newport, but the request had been apparently refused and two other men had been sent.'

By his will of 21 April 1647, Daniel Harvey left £1,000 to his brother, William. (Paget, C.G., 1929, 35; Cope, 1959, i, 1250.) Two years later, i.e., in 1649, Jean Riolan, Jun., (c. 1577–1657), Dean of the Paris Faculty of Medicine, who had become Regius Professor of Anatomy and Botany in 1613, and later had been appointed Physician-in-Chief to the Queen-Mother of France, Marie de Medicis (mother-in-law of King Charles I), produced his work, entitled, *Encheiridium anatomicum et pathologicum*, which set the limits for Riolan's acceptance of a circulation. These were in the main its restriction to certain parts only of the body, and the old idea that blood passed through the interventricular septum. Riolan had been known to Harvey personally for some time and was an outstanding figure in the world of medicine of his day; he also sent Harvey a presentation copy of his new work, which reveals him as a modified Galenist in respect of the circulation. In the only defence which he ever made to criticisms of *De motu cordis et sanguinis in animalibus*, 1628, Harvey published a courteous reply to Riolan in his own *De circulatione sanguinis*, which in its Latin version of 1649 was a simultaneous production by Roger David in Cambridge and by Arnold Leers in Rotterdam respectively, and consisted of two essays.

The former of these included an altogether remarkable passage defining physiology, and stating its position in medical learning with typical Harveian precision. The contemplation of those things which are normal, he wrote, 'is physiology, and it is the first thing to be learned by medical men. For that which is normal is right and serves as a criterion for both itself and the abnormal. By defining in its light departures from it and unnatural reactions, pathology becomes more clearly obvious for the future, and from pathology the practice and art of healing, and opportunities for discovering multiple new remedies, derive.

Riolan had chosen as his own task the demonstration of the seats of all diseases, an effort becoming the leading anatomist, said Harvey, though he appeared to be doubtful about the possibility of showing from the cadavers of *healthy* subjects the sites of diseases, and the value of listing what others thought must be the appearances of disease in those places. Harvey felt that such example set by Riolan determined him himself to take corresponding action, and to indite and commit similarly to writing his, Harvey's, medical analysis also, 'so that from many dissections of patients dying of very severe and remarkable complaints [he] should undertake an account of the ways and manners in which the internal parts change in site, size, constitution, figure, substance, and other appreciable variables from the natural form and appearance commonly described by all anatomists, and the various remarkable ways in which they are affected.' According to Herringham (1929, 19), however, Harvey's clinical and post-mortem notes which he had had in 1648 when the essays to Riolan were written, are unfortunately lost. The rest of the first essay to him needs to be read at greater length, yet one can at least admire his example of thanks to a fellow-author, which runs, 'For the rest, Riolan, I congratulate both myself and yourself, myself because of the significance with which you have invested the circulation, yourself on a learned, polished and concise book of unsurpassed elegance, for the gift of which to me I thank you most fully, the deserved praises of which I both should and would like to recount; I confess, however, that I am unequal to so great a task.'

The second essay 'in which many objections to the circuit of the blood are refuted', said that 'It is now many [i.e., 21] years ago, learned Riolan, since with the assistance of the press I published a part of my work. Since that birthday of the circuit of the blood there has of a truth been scarcely a day, or even the smallest interval of time passing, in which I have not heard both good and ill report of the circulation which I discovered. Some tear the as yet tender infant to bits with their wranglings, as undeserving of birth: others by contrast consider that the offspring ought to be nurtured, and cherish it and protect it by their writings. The former oppose it with strong dislike, the latter defend it vociferously. These think that by means of experiments, observations, and my own visual experiments I have established the circuit of the blood against the whole strength and force of arguments; the others that it is scarcely as yet sufficiently elucidated, and not yet freed from objections. There are moreover those who cry out that I have striven after the empty glory of vivisections, and they disparage and ridicule with childish levity the frogs, snakes, flies, and other lower animals which I have brought on to my stage. Nor do they abstain from scurrilous language.'

'To return scurrility with scurrility, however,' went on Harvey, 'I judge unworthy in a philosopher and searcher after truth. I think it will be better and wiser to tone down these many indications of bad manners by the light of true and trustworthy indications. It is unavoidable that dogs bark and vomit their surfeit, or cynics are numbered among the assembled philosophers, but one must take care that they do not bite, or kill with their savage madness, or gnaw with a canine tooth the very bones and foundations of truth. While I resolved with myself that censurers, mummers, and stain-defiled writers of disapprobations should never be read (as being men from whom nothing sound or remarkable except scurrility was to be expected), I judged them even less worthy of answer. Let them enjoy their evil nature: I think they will scarcely ever have well-disposed readers: and the good God does not give to the wicked that which is most outstanding and most to be desired, namely, wisdom. Let them continue,' he concluded, 'with their scurrility until it irks if it does not shame them, and finally tires them out.'

After many pages of addition to the circulatory knowledge adduced in his 1628 book, Harvey went on to describe very succinctly some of the variations observed. 'For what is more remarkable than the way in which our body reacts differently in every affection, appetite, hope, or fear, and the countenance itself changes, and the blood appears to be escaping hither or thither? The eyes redden with anger and the pupil is constricted. In bashfulness, the cheeks are lavish with blushes: in fear, disgrace, and shame, the face is pale but the ears are red as if about to hear ill; in adolescents touched with desire, how quickly is the penis filled with blood, erected and extended?' Side by side with this word about the human male it is fitting to place (from *De generatione animalium*, in *Opera omnia*, 1766, 564) Harvey's semi-poetical words about the developing human female: 'It is equally well known what change occurs in a virgin with the first growth and warming of the uterus, for she comes to puberty, acquires a richer complexion, undergoes enlargement of her breasts, becomes more beautiful in looks and her eyes glitter; her voice becomes melodious, her gait, gestures and speech all take on elegance; and severe illnesses are cured at this very time or never.'

From the surrender of Oxford to the Parliamentary Forces in 1646, Harvey returned to London, and he seems to have lived with one or other of his immediate relatives. He was frequently at Coombe, Croydon, Surrey, which had formerly belonged to his brother, Daniel Harvey. Daniel and Eliab Harvey had been assessed for loans of £5,000 and £2,500 respectively by the Parliamentary Committee for the Advance of Money, but Daniel refused to pay his assessment, and on 23 November 1643 he was ordered to be taken into custody. On 5 April 1644 his rents, goods, and estate were ordered to be seized and sold, and in the following month he was committed in custody to Lambeth House, and was ordered to be sent by sea to Plymouth and kept there until his assessment was paid. But on 4 November he was released from Lambeth on payment of £400 and his undertaking to abide by the Committee's decision as to the residue. He paid £1,000 four days later, and eventually on 20 December 1644, having paid in all £3,000, he was ordered to pay a further £1,000 in six weeks, after which he would have the Public Faith and be discharged from his obligation.

Daniel did not long survive his ordeal, for his death was presented at a Court of the Manor of Croydon, held on 24 October 1647, and his son Daniel inherited the Coombe estate as a minor in the custody of his mother. Aubrey the historian says that William Harvey did 'delight to be in the dark, and could then best contemplate . . . whilst at the house at Coombe in Surrey he had caves made in the ground in which he delighted in summer-time to meditate.'

It was towards the end of 1650 that Harvey was visited by his friend, Dr George Ent, and Dr Ent can well be allowed to tell his own story, in other words, the Epistle Dedicatory which he wrote for Harvey's long *De generatione animalium*, 1651. It read: 'To the distinguished and eminent President and Fellows of the College of Physicians of London, George Ent sends warmest greetings!

'Last Christmas, while still weary of anxious and, as it was to prove, not very profitable care, I strove to remove that cloud from my spirit, and accordingly visited that great man and chief glory and ornament of our College, Harvey I mean, who was at that time staying not far from the City. I found him intent on examining the nature of things, and Democritus-like investigating everything with a cheerful countenance and a quick mind. I then at once greeted him with "Are all things sufficiently well with you?" "How can they be," he replied, "when the common-wealth is full of troubles, and I myself am still all at sea? And indeed," he added, "were I not refreshed by the comfort of my studies and the recollection of the things I once observed, I [should] have no reason for wishing to live any longer. So it has come to pass that this sheltered life and freedom from public cares, which is wont to cause sickness of mind in others, has brought healing to myself." Here I, interrupting, said: "I will explain why that is so. It is so because most men's wisdom is based on the brain of others, and they retail as their own wares the traditional ones (supplemented by a display of different phrasing and new method). You yourself, on the other hand, have ever preferred to consult Nature herself about her own secrets. Moreover, such study, while less misleading, is also more pleasurable inasmuch as, while one is making a particular investigation, others often occur to one quite unsought. You yourself (I remember) used sometimes to tell me that you had never planned the dissection of any animal (and you have planned the dissection of very many) without discovering in it something unexpected, of which you had no previous thought."

' "It is so," he said, "I have always thought it right to look at the animals themselves, and I have imagined that we could obtain from them not only some of the lesser secrets of Nature, but even some inkling of the Supreme Creator himself. And, though many things were discovered by learned men of yore, I should imagine that many more are still buried in the dark night of unexplored Nature. I have indeed often wondered or even laughed at those who believe that everything has been so perfected and completed by Aristotle, Galen, or some other great person that not a single jot can be added to his account. Nature certainly is a most reliable interpreter of her own secrets, and the things she shows more sparingly or more obscurely in one kind of animal she explains more clearly and more openly in another one. No one, indeed, will rightly have settled the function or office of any part without in several animals having seen its structure, position, vascular connections and other features, and having carefully pondered over them. The early philosophers confined their knowledge of regions, as also of animals, plants and other matters almost entirely to Greece. But we have open to us the whole world, and through the zeal of travellers not only have we become acquainted with the places and the habits and customs of the inhabitants, but we have also come to know the animals of each region, and its product of minerals and of plants. No race is so savage but that, either through chance or the drive of some urgent need, it will have devised for the common weal something which has escaped the notice of other, more civilized nations. But are we to imagine nothing further as accruing from these advantages to the great domains of learning, that all knowledge was rapidly absorbed right from very early times? For such an end result we must certainly blame our own laziness, not Nature."

' "There is another, further trouble. Often many men lacking in experience get an idea of another's probable view, and later give it out boldly as definitely true. Hence it comes about that they not only err themselves, but lead imprudent other people astray."

'While he was discoursing on these and other similar matters with the wonderful facility that he displays, I interrupted to say, "How free you yourself are from this fault is sufficiently well appreciated by all who know you. Hence most learned men who have studied your unremitting labour in the increase of knowledge eagerly await your further experiments." Harvey smilingly said, "Do you really wish once again to send me out into the treacherous sea away from the peace of this haven in which I pass my life? You know well how much trouble my earlier studies evoked. It is far sounder to pass the time wisely and privately at home than to publish unduly soon what you have collected with much labour, and [thereby] to stir up storms which will in due course ruin your peace and quiet." "Truly," I replied, "it is the common reward of well-doing for good deserts to be poorly paid. But the winds which, like the northeaster, raise up those tempests bring destruction in their own train."

'Simultaneously he showed me the essays, elaborated by vast effort, on the generation of animals. "There," I said, "I have what I was wanting. Unless you are agreeable to make them public, I shall say that you are unjust to both your own repute and the advantage of others. And there will be no trouble for you to deal with in the matter. For I will myself willingly take on all the proof-correcting."

'Embarrassed though he was at first, and saying among other things that there would be a gap caused by the loss of the volume containing the account of the generation of insects, I succeeded finally in getting his consent. "And I grant you," he said, "full authority either to publish these my writings straightway or to suppress them to a later date."

'Thanking him most warmly for so great a gift, I said good-bye to him and went off like another Jason, enriched by a golden fleece. After getting home, I took a quick look at my booty, and I was amazed that so vast a treasure had remained hidden and concealed for so long; that, while others proudly display their trifles and nonsense and their twice or a hundred times re-heated dishes, this really great man assesses so lightly his outstanding observations. Indeed, so often as he produces new discoveries, he does not behave as many folk do and regard them as something extraordinary or inspired. On the contrary, he acts as if he had happened on those matters by chance or by a simple stroke of business, though he has in fact devoted much work and unceasing study to them. It is evidence of his extreme brilliance that he impugns the reputation of no author, but everywhere [just] quietly puts forward his own opinion. He is indeed wont to say that it is a sign of an ill cause to [have to] struggle quarrelsomely and contentiously for victory in it, while truth on the other hand needs no defender. And, though he could readily have clothed the whole of this work in materials of his own making, he preferred to avoid a charge of envy and to follow the lead of Aristotle and of Aquapendente, as if he himself were merely adding the remaining woof.

'I will not pursue that line, lest I seem to praise to his face one who is over and above all the praise that I can bestow; especially shall I not do it to you Fellows of the College to whom Harvey's work, splendour, and genius are so well known. About myself I will add only this one note, that in so far as this business is concerned I have merely performed the office of a midwife. That is, I have brought to the light of day this foetus such as you see it, finished and perfected but having labour difficulty, and perhaps fearing some adverse draught. I have, I admit, been in charge of the press and our author is wont to write (it's a custom among our learned men, they say) such a fist that no one without practice can easily read it. I have, therefore, taken great trouble to prevent many mistakes in *this* published work. In the one our author published not so long ago, less trouble—I see—was [in fact] taken.

'You have thus, Gentlemen, the reason for this address. It is so that you may know that our Harvey has made a present for the benefit of the republic of letters, for the honour of all of you, and for his own satisfaction. Farewell, and prosper!'

Munk's *Roll of the Royal College of Physicians* states that Harvey is said to have written

> *Observationes de usu lienis*
> *Observationes de motu locali*
> *Tractatus physiologicus*
> *Observationes medicinales*
> *De amore, libidine et coitu animalium,*

none of which was [in 1861] known to be in existence.

The *Biographia Britannica*, 1797, however, suggests that among his writings was a treatise conformable to his doctrine of the circulation of the blood, and *that* would have been particularly interesting. But we must be content with D'Arcy Power's final words in 1897. 'We thus take our leave of one of the master minds of the seventeenth century. Harvey's osteological lecture has not yet been found, and many of his investigations in comparative anatomy are still wanting. But there is a possibility that his papers and books were only dispersed, and were not destroyed, at the pillage of his lodgings in Whitehall. Some of the wreckage is still cast up from time to time, and we may hope that more may yet be found. Every fragment of his work is interesting,' and little did one imagine, but a little while back, that Harvey's correspondence with Caspar Hofmann had got into Albrecht von Haller's library and would be discovered in 1960 in the Bibliotheca Brera by Dr Ercole Ferrario.

But I personally do not wish to lose an opportunity of quoting from the memorable passage which is to be found in the words beginning 'Neupe agnoseimus Deum . . .' on pp. 419–20 of the 1766 Edition of his collected works. In translation it reads, 'I do indeed acknowledge God, the supreme and almighty Creator, as being universally present in the production of all animals and indicated in his works. Indeed, in such generation everything is constructed and fashioned with unexampled foresight, divine wisdom and wonderful skill. And these attributes befit only the Almighty source of all things, by whichever name he prefers to be called—the divine Mind as Aristotle has it; the soul of the world according to Plato; essential nature, according to others; in the pagan concepts Saturn or Jove; or rather as I myself find becoming, the Creator and Father of all things in heaven and in earth, on whom animals and their beginnings depend, by whose will or edict everything comes into being and is begotten.'

Had Harvey lived but a few years longer, he would doubtless have been one of the original Fellows of the Royal Society of London for improving Natural Knowledge, with the motto taken from Horace's *Epistles* 'Nullius in Verba'. In full the original reads

> *Ac ne porte rogas, quo me duce, quo lare tuter*
> *Nullius addictus iurare in verba magistri,*
> *Quo me cumque rapit tempestas, deferor hospes*

> (Lest you should chance to ask what leader I
> follow or what godhead guards me, I am not bound
> to revere the word of any particular master;
> but where the wind carries me, I put into port
> and make myself at home.)[1]

After a recent talk on King Charles I and William Harvey at the Royal Society of Medicine, the speaker was asked why the King had never given an honour to Harvey. To which a proper answer could have been that the King had made Harvey Warden of Merton College, while earlier he had commissioned, and presented to him, a portrait in oils by

---

[1] And according to Andrade (1960) it constituted a very clear indication that the Society cut loose from the authority of Aristotle and the other masters of antiquity.

William Dobson (1610–46), of Charles, Prince of Wales, aged 12. The picture was continuously in possession of Harvey or his relatives until 1934, when it passed to the Scottish National Portrait Gallery. A colour print of it was the generous gift of A. Dickson Wright, Esq., M.S., F.R.C.S., the altogether inspiring President of the Harvey Tercentenary Congress of 1959, when I brought out a translated edition of *The Circulation of the Blood* and of nine letters written by Harvey.

I close with words written by Nardi in 1658: *Sed iam prima mei pars est exacta laboris.*

De generatione animalium had certainly taken shape, Keynes (1928) thought, by 1649, and it appeared in four editions (a London one by Pulleyn in quarto, and three Amsterdam ones by Elzevir, Janssen and Ravensteyn respectively in duodecimo) in 1651. It is a link between Harvey as a young man assisting Fabricius at Padua[1] and the mature and ageing scientist, who in his section 'De partu' of the book provided, according to Herbert Spencer (1921) the first English textbook of Midwifery, etc. As this was a notable achievement, I have copied fairly freely from Spencer's Harveian Oration and have employed my own translation of 'De partu', less from 'opificem evadere' on p. 596 of Harvey's *Opera omnia*, 1766, onwards.

In his 1920 Harveian Oration the late Sir Frederick Andrewes said of *De generatione animalium* that 'if the most instructive part of this treatise is perhaps the introduction on

---

[1] *De generatione animalium*, in *Opera omnia*, 1766, Ex. 6, 206, read, 'Ego tamen aliquando (ut hic Fabricio patrocinio parem) verna tempestate (de coitus foecundantis tempore et necessitate aliquid certi indagaturus) gallinas duas a gallo seclusas per quatriduum detinui, quae interea singulae tria ova pepererant, non minus aliis ovis prolifica. Iterumque aliam gallinam seclusi, quae decimo ab inde die ovum paperit; aliudque die vicesimo, et utrumque foecundum, ut videatur, posse unum atque alterum coitum, integrum racemum, omnique illius anni ova foecunda reddere.'

scientific method, it necessarily follows that the work cannot contain any outstanding contributions in embryology. Here Harvey in his later age sets forth the principles which had guided him, with Aristotle as his leader, in his life's work, and we realize how truly scientific were his methods. But though these methods enabled him to correct many of the errors of his predecessors, and though the *De Generatione* is full of accurate and curious observations and good reasoning, in comparison with the *De Motu Cordis*, it leaves us cold. No great conclusion emerges; the real problems of generation remain unsolved. And no wonder; Harvey had no microscope.'

Sir Henry Dale wrote that *De generatione animalium* contains a wealth of careful and accurate observations in the two series dealing with the development of the chicken on the successive days of incubation, and with the appearance and development of the foetal deer on successive days after impregnation of the doe or the hind. Harvey's description of the earlier stages of embryogeny, and especially of placentation in the Cervidae, for the observation of which his royal master and patient allowed him to have unrivalled opportunity, might, one feels, gain a new interest, if edited and interpreted in the light of the comparative knowledge of these processes, which has been so greatly extended in recent years. . . . And though his description of the origin and development of the chick deals faithfully with the somewhat fantastic errors of his teacher Fabricius and others of his predecessors, it cannot stand with that which Malpighi was to send to the Royal Society some twenty-two years later, and which remained with remarkably little need of change for another two centuries.

After Dale's contribution come three books by Professor William Meyer, of Sanford University, which require mention, particularly his 1936 work, *An analysis of the* De generatione animalium *of William Harvey*, though one can well refer also to his 1939 and 1956 publications, entitled 'The rise of embryology' and 'Human Generation' respectively. I wish also to mention the late Dr H. P. Bayon's essay of 1947 on Harvey's application of biological experiment, clinical observation, and comparative anatomy to the problems of generation. I give as a last reference a very recent, beautifully illustrated paper by Hamilton, Harrison and Young on 'Aspects of placentation in certain cervidae', which appeared in *J. Anat. Lond.*, *94*, 1–33.

For his 1936 work Meyer had a completely new but as yet (I believe) unpublished translation made of Harvey's *De generatione animalium*, but I have not seen a copy of the translation. Meyer said that the *De generatione* was great in purpose, but the *De motu cordis* was that also in accomplishment. None of the editions referred to by Meyer appeared shortly before the revival of interest in embryology, and Meyer doubted if it could be shown that that revival was due to influences deriving from Harvey. 'Although the *De Generatione* may well have been the chief interest of his life, the *De Motu*, no doubt, will always be regarded as the crowning glory of it.'

Bayon wrote that 'it would be absurd to assert that if Harvey had not written *De generatione* (1651) medicine and biology could not have reached the present stage of progressive knowledge. It is reasonable to suggest, however, that the incentive provided by Harvey resulted in the first experiments by Redi, then those of John Turberville Needham and Spallanzani, and in this manner indicated the path to be followed.'

He adds, incidentally, that it can be recalled that in Ex. 57 Harvey said that he had noted the inflammatory reaction resulting from scratching of the hand with clean and dirty needles respectively. 'The description,' said Bayon, 'is one of the first records of the experimental approach to pathology.'

Further on he discussed Harvey's pathfinding experimental study of mammalian embryogeny and said that 'if one excepts the legendary observations on female slaves made by Queen Cleopatra—as related in the Talmud—Harvey, by tests on deer in Windsor Park and at Hampton Court, was the first in the field to observe and record the development of mammalian embryos'; though 'he was singularly unfortunate in the choice of subject, because among *Cervidae* there is a considerable lag between fertilization and the naked-eye appearance of the concept', though 'this was not ascertained till the middle of the 19th century, after prolonged studies by Bischoff, 1854, on the roe—*Cervus caprcolus*.'

Bayon's paper is well worth a longer reading than this brief account of it attempts to give. He summarized by saying that 'the majority of modern critics consider *De motu* (1628) far superior to *De generatione* (1651); nonetheless, the two works can be evenly compared, because merits and flaws are evident in both. For in both Harvey made an initial attempt to correlate the lessons of clinical observation, biological demonstrative experiment, and comparative anatomy, and then reported truthfully on what he saw. It can be conceded that the demonstration of the mechanical circulation of the blood yielded correct even if incomplete results, while the pioneer observations and tests on does in Windsor Park did not. Indeed, the choice of animals with an abnormal embryogeny ended by enmeshing Harvey in futile speculation. . . . Still—by examining embryogeny in mammals, by postulating the universal origin of living animals from eggs, by reformulating the Aristotelian doctrine of epigenesis, by doubting the occurrence of spontaneous generation—all these opinions, however faultily pronounced, provided the correct incentive for those investigations that achieved the triumphs of contemporary biological medicine. It is suggested that in the history of medical progress the significance of both these books is equally great;

a study of both is essential to obtain a clear conception of Harvey's personality.'

Between 1651 and 1657 Harvey wrote eight letters to correspondents abroad, and about these eight men we have a little detail. The first was addressed on 26 March 1651 to Paul Marquard Schlegel, of Hamburg, a strong supporter of Harvey's views on the circulation, who had been born on 23 August 1605 in that city, and had taken up the study of natural and medical sciences against the wishes of his father, a prosperous merchant of the city. He had begun such work in Altdorf in 1626, well before he can have known much about Harvey, but later had moved to Wittenberg, where he was attached to his later to be famous fellow-countryman, Werner Rolfinck (1599–1673); when in 1629 Rolfinck had become Professor of Anatomy and Botany in Jena, Schlegel had followed him thither. In 1631 he had undertaken a scientific journey which in the event lasted several years, Holland and England being the first two countries visited. From England he had gone to France, whence after a fairly long stay in Paris, Lyon and Montpellier he had moved on to Italy. After visiting Rome and Naples he had returned home to Germany, where he had at once become Professor of Botany, Anatomy and Surgery in Jena. In 1642 he was called to Hamburg to be Chief Physician there. He died on 20 February 1653. In 1650, at Hamburg, he had produced *De sanguinis motu commentatio, in qua praecipue in Joannis Riolani sententiam inquiritur.* This publication is well worth reading; in it Schlegel attacked the ideas of his former teacher, Jean Riolan, Jun., about the functions of the portal vein. The finding on a throttled man which is mentioned in the second paragraph of Harvey's letter to Schlegel is an important piece in the total circulatory story told by the former.

The letter opens by Harvey congratulating Schlegel on his dissertation against his erstwhile teacher, the famous Riolan, which made unnecessary what Harvey himself had been planning to write, but had been glad to omit as he had been busy publishing *De generatione animalium*, of which he sends Schlegel a copy. He refers to Schlegel's own 'most exquisite little book (which I am not unduly praising by referring to it in such terms)', which he regards as an excellent reply to Riolan's attacks on the Harveian ideas of the circulation. He says that a circuit of the blood occurs in very many blood-containing animals devoid of lungs. If the artery-like vein and the vein-like artery and the aorta are ligated in the cadaver of a throttled human being, and the left ventricle is opened, a forcible injection of water via the vena cava causes swelling of the left ventricle and auricle, but no escape of warm water via the gap in the left ventricle. When the ligatures mentioned had been released, the same arrangements for injection of fluid had been made through a tube tied into the artery-like vein with a tight ligature preventing fluid from getting back through it into the right ventricle. Under these conditions fluid came from the left ventricle pari passu with each injection into the artery-like vein. With which single experiment, so often as he wishes to repeat it, Schlegel will easily have silenced all Riolan's arguments about the matter. It was doubtless fitting for the Dean of the College of Paris to keep Galen's medicine in good repair and to allow no innovation to enter his school lest the precepts and dogmata of the physicians be disturbed and lest the pathology which, with their agreement, has obtained for so many years in assigning the causes of diseases, be corrupted. Other matters occupy the rest of the long letter from Harvey.

On 4 July 1651 the President of the College of Physicians (Dr Francis Prujean) read to the Fellows assembled at an Extraordinary Commitia a letter in which the writer (who proved eventually to be Harvey) said: 'If I can produce one that will build a library and a repository for simples and rarities, such a one as shall be suitable and honourable to the

College, will you assent to have it done or no, and give me leave and such others as I shall desire to be the designers and overlookers of the work both for conveniency and ornament?' It is not surprising that all went at once to record their votes in favour, and the story will shortly be continued.

But first one can note the sending of the second of the series of Harvey's letters abroad, this one going off on 15 July to Doctor Giovanni Nardi, of Florence, with apologies from the writer for not having written [sooner] partly because of the civil war or 'the public troubles', as they are euphemistically called, partly because of business connected with the publishing of the book on the generation of animals.

Work on the library at Amen Corner went on apace, and the name of the donor became known for, before its completion, the College on 22 December 1652 voted that a statue of him should be placed in the Hall. This was accordingly done, and an inscription on the pedestal read:

Gulielmo Harveio
Viro monumentis suis immortali
Hoc insuper Collegium Medicorum Londinense
posuit,
Qui enim sanguini motum
ut et
Animalibus ortum dedit,
Meruit esse
Stator perpetuus.

It showed Harvey in the cap and gown of his degree and, though it was destroyed in the Great Fire of London in 1666, it was not replaced when the College was rebuilt at or near its old site, nor more recently in its Pall Mall East building (the move was in 1825; see Payne, L.M., 1960).

The library building for which Harvey was responsible at Amen Corner was described by Aubrey as a noble one of Roman architecture (though it seems strange that it was detailed as 'of rustique work with Corinthian pillasters') consisting of a great parlour, a kind of Convocation house for the Fellows to meet in, below; and a library above. On the frieze outside, in letters three inches long, was an inscription saying that the structure had been begun in 1653, when Francis Prujean was President and Edmund Smith an Elect.

Harvey not only paid for the building, but furnished its library with books on astronomy, geometry, geography, music, optics, natural history, and travels, as well as those upon medical topics. The museum contained various objects of curiosity and a variety also of surgical instruments. It was formally opened on 2 February 1653, when Harvey received the President and Fellows at a sumptuous entertainment, and thereafter in a speech made over to the College the title-deeds and his whole interest in the structure and its contents.

Some time in 1652 Harvey probably made his will, and on 28 April he wrote the third of his series of letters, this one being addressed to Dr Robert Morison, of Paris. According to the D.N.B., Morison was M.A., PH.D. (Aberdeen) at twenty but, after bearing arms in the Royalist cause, went to Paris and became a physician and botanist and got to know Charles II, whom he accompanied to England at the Restoration, and by whom he was appointed his Senior Physician, King's Botanist, and Superintendent of all the royal gardens. The rest of his life was botanical and medical, in Oxford.

Harvey's letter to Morison necessitates a word or two about the lacteals and the thoracic duct, and also about Gasparo Aselli (1581–1626) and Jean Pecquet (1622–74). Aselli discovered the lacteals in 1622, but did not publish his finding until 1627, i.e., posthumously, and erred in making his 'lacteal veins' end in the liver. Jean Pecquet, while still a student in the University of Montpellier, discovered the thoracic duct in 1647 in an animal opened during dissection, and in many experiments traced it caudally and discovered its origin in the receptaculum chyli, into which the lacteals empty. Tracing it in the other direction, he found its termination in the subclavian vein. He published in 1651, and Van Horne, who had been working independently of him, corroborated his findings in 1652.

Harvey congratulated himself that Pecquet had confirmed the Harveian view about the circulation by such sure experiments and clear reasonings. He could, however, have wished that Pecquet had noticed a triple movement of the heart, to wit, a systole of contractile and expulsive character, then a reversal of this, and finally a diastole in which the ventricles are filled and distended by blood coming from the auricles immediately prior to systole. Harvey had known about the lacteals before Aselli had published his small book about them, and he goes on to discuss problems about the chyle.

In his *Examen academiarum* of 1653, Webster wrote that 'We are teaching nothing but Galen though our never sufficiently honoured countryman Dr Harvey has advanced the study of Anatomy', and on 30 November Harvey wrote again to Dr Giovanni Nardi, of Florence, and said that it was a joy to see that Nardi had attributed almost the same efficient cause to plague as he, Harvey, had to the generation of animals.

On 1 February 1654–55, Harvey penned his first letter to Dr Johann Daniel Horst, Chief Physician of Hesse-Darmstadt, who had been born at Giessen in 1616, and had become Professor and Court Physician there in 1637; he was destined to live until 1685. Harvey congratulated himself 'that after so long a lapse of time and despite such a separation in space' Horst had preserved his memory of him. 'With regard to Riolan's opinion and his view about the circulation of the blood,' said Harvey devastatingly, 'he has very obviously achieved mighty trifles by great effort and I cannot see that his fictions have brought pleasure to anyone. Schlegel wrote more carefully and modestly and, had the fates permitted, would doubtless have taken the force out of Riolan's arguments and even out of his taunts. But I learn, and that with sorrow, that he shuffled off this mortal coil of ours a few months since.' The things Horst asks him about the lacteal veins and thoracic ducts demand sharp-sighted eyes and a mind free from other cares, two perquisites no longer available to Harvey. He finishes this letter with,

'Farwell, learned Sir, and live happily
   As your
      heartily devoted
         William Harvey wishes that you may!'

In 1654 the College unanimously chose Harvey as its President when Dr Prujean's term came to an end on Michaelmas Day, and two of the Elects waited upon him to learn his answer; he thanked them for the very high honour, but asked to decline on the grounds of age and infirmity, and suggested instead that they should re-appoint Dr Prujean to this, the highest place among the physicians of England. They followed his good advice, and his first act was to nominate Harvey one of the Consiliarii—an office which he accepted and to which he was reappointed in 1655 and 1656.

Harvey's second letter to Horst was dated 13 July 1655 and said that he had recently rewritten, for Horst's gratification, the replies he had made earlier to Morison's requests for his views on the lacteal veins and thoracic ducts. 'Not indeed,' he said, 'because I was certain of the correctness of the view I advanced, but so that I might with those various objections twist a little the ears of those who think that they have revealed all on the basis of a very few discoveries only.' 'The vagitus uterinus,' or 'crying in utero,' mentioned by Harvey in this letter to Horst, was historically reviewed by G. H. Ryder (1943), who found 122 well-authenticated cases in the literature up to that date; further reference is found in Russell and others (1957). Nathanael Highmore (1613–85), who is mentioned in this second letter to Horst, was the author of *Corporis humani disquisitio anatomica*, 1651, The Hague, the first English anatomical work in which the circulation had been fully recognized, but he did not live in the part from which this letter to Horst had been written, nor had Harvey seen him for over seven years.

When the Harveian library was opened, Christopher Merrett (1614–95), a friend of Harvey, was living in the College House at Amen Corner, and had just been granted a twenty-one years' lease at an annual rent of £20. All agreed that he was a suitable person for the post of library keeper, not only because of his residence on the spot, but because of his general scientific entertainments. He was accordingly nominated to the post by Harvey. His services in connection with the opening of the library were very soon recognized, for in June 1654 it was resolved that from the 26th of that month, Merrett should be 'discharged from paying any rent for his dwelling house, from all quit-rent also, and taxations for the College, till such time as provision be made for him by some other equivalent way.' Meanwhile he had to keep the house in repair and observe such statutes as should be made concerning the library. He was one of an interesting group of physicians and botanical students who were up at Oxford at the same time (Gunther, 1936), his own College being Oriel, and he was later one of the original Fellows of the Royal Society.

Harvey last attended the College on 30 September 1656. On that day he had been elected Consiliarius for the third time, but provision was made 'that if Dr Harvey should happen to be absent at any time because of ill-health Dr Prujean should take his place'. Harvey himself must have been aware of his declining strength, for two months earlier he had resigned the office of Lumleian Lecturer and at the same time announced a further gift to the College.

On 24 July 1656 he entertained all the Fellows together with some friends to a magnificent banquet and formally handed over the deeds of his patrimonial estate at Burmarsh in Kent. In making this gift Harvey made provision for the library keeper and intended that there should be instituted an annual feast at which a Latin oration should be spoken 'to commemorate the benefactors of the College and to exhort the Fellows to study and search out the secrets of nature by way of experiment, and also, for the honour of the profession, to continue in love and affection among themselves.' The proceedings were brought to an end by eloquent and vigorous speeches by the President (Dr Edward Alston), Dr Edward Emily, and Dr Charles Scarburgh.

The surrender of Oxford marks the period of Harvey's severance from the Court and also the year in which his wife died. Not long before this, he had lost his twin brothers, Matthew and Michael, and his second brother, John. It is not, therefore, surprising that he elected, at the age of sixty-eight and a martyr to gout, to retire from public life and spend the closing years of his life either in London or in the country at the house of one of his brothers, Eliab (1589–1661) or Daniel (1587–1657). Eliab had a house at Roehampton and reminiscences which are in the College's possession refer to some of the habits of Harvey as communicated to William Heberden (1710–1801). With the spelling unchanged, the note reads:

'1761, May 29. Mrs. Harvey (great niece to Dr Harvey) told me that the Dr lived at his brother's at Roehampton, the later part of his life. That he used to walk out in a morning combing his head in the fields.

'That he was humoursome, & would sit down exactly at the same time he had appointed for dinner, whether the company were come, or not.

'That his saltseller was always fill'd with sugar, which he used to eat instead of salt.

'That if the gout was very painful to him in the night, he would rise & put his feet into cold water.'

Harvey's third letter to Doctor Giovanni Nardi, of Florence, was addressed to him from London on 25 October 1655, and called him 'a gentleman of outstanding worth, manners, and learning'. He asks if Nardi received safely his sendings of 'a long time ago' [? of 30 November 1653], and says he would like to know how far he has advanced with his *Noctes geniales* and the other works on which he had resolved. 'For I am wont to enliven my now rather inactive old age, and my spirit which scorns the trifles of everyday, by reading the best books of that kind.'

Thanks to the kindness of the Librarian of the Royal Society of Medicine, I have been able to see a photostatic copy of the section of *Noctes geniales* which is said to give a discussion of Harvey's discovery. I also thank the Assistant Librarian of the Royal College of Physicians who loaned the book for photographing. But I have, to my regret, no very worthwhile outcome of my labours to communicate.

Harvey mentioned two of his nephews in his letter to Nardi, and referred to one of them as his 'favourite nephew'. But I cannot elucidate further.

The last in the series of letters written by Harvey to correspondents abroad was addressed 'to the distinguished and elegant gentleman and experienced physician, Jan Vlackveld, of Haarlem' on 24 April, not over-long before Harvey's death.

The only reference I have found to Vlackveld is a note to the effect that his doctorate thesis had been entitled *De caco-chymia*. The opening lines of the second paragraph of Harvey's letter to him ('Nature is nowhere wont to reveal her innermost secrets more openly than where she shows faint traces of herself away from the beaten track.') were extremely apposite to the work of the late Sir Archibald

124

Garrod on the inborn errors of metabolism, and were so quoted by him in his Harveian Oration of 1924 on 'The debt of science to medicine'.

Wishing to recall Harvey's manner of dying, I looked up what Aubrey had said, and re-read that 'after Oxford was surrendered, which was 24 July, 1646, he [Harvey] came to London, and lived with his brother Eliab, a rich merchant in London, on [? St Lawrence Poultney] hill, opposite to St Lawrence, Poultry . . . and at his brother's country house at Roe-hampton. His brother Eliab bought, about 1654, Cockaine-house, now (1680) the Excise-Office, a noble house, where the Doctor was wont to contemplate on the leads of the house, and had his severall stations, in regard of the Sun, or wind . . . He was pretty well versed in Mathematiques, and had made himself master of Mr Oughtred's Clavis math. in his old age; and I have seen him perusing it, and working problems not long before he dyed, and the book was always in his meditating apartment. His chamber was in that room which is now the office of Elias Ashmole, Esq., where he dyed: being taken with the dead palsey, which took away his speech; as soon as he was attaqued, he presently sent for his brother, and nephews, and gave one a watch,[1] another another thing, &c. as remembrances of him. He dyed worth 20000 l. wch he left to his brother Eliab. In his will he left his old friend Mr. Tho. Hobbes 10 l. as a token of his love. He was wont to say, that man was but a great mischievous baboon. . . .' Elsewhere Aubrey said, 'I well remember that Dr. Alsop at his Funerall sayd . . . that he was 80, wanting one . . . He lies buried in a vault at Hempsted in Essex, wch his brother Eliab Harvey built; he is lapt in lead, and on his brest in great letters DR. WILLIAM HARVEY. I was at his Funerall, and helpt to carry him into the vault.'

[1] Elsewhere, Aubrey said, ' 'Twas a minute watch, wth wch he made his experiments.'

Aubrey recalled that 'Harvey was always very contemplative, and the first y^t I heare of y^t was curious in Anatomie in England. He had made dissections of froggs, toades, and a number of other animals, and had curious observations on them.' He also brings into the story a person who has previously been mentioned more than once in this present book, for he says that Harvey 'was physician, and a great favourite of the Lord High Marshall of England, Thomas Howard, Earl of Arundel and Surrey, with whom he travelled in his Ambassade to the Emperor . . . at Vienna, A.D. 163 [6].

'Harvey,' Aubrey went on, 'was much and often troubled with the gowte, and his way of cure was thus; he would sitt with his legges bare, if it were frost, on the leads of Cockaine house, putt them in a payle of water, till he was almost dead with cold, and betake himselfe to his stove, and so 'twas gone.

'He was hott-headed, and his thoughts working would many times keep him from sleeping; he told me, that then his way was, to rise out of his bed, and walke about his chamber in his shirt, till he was pretty coole, i.e., till he began to have a horror [i.e., a shuddering or shivering], and then returne to his bed, and sleep very comfortably.'

In passing, Aubrey said, 'I remember he was wont to drinke coffee; which he and his brother Eliab did, before coffee-houses were in fashion in London.

'All his profession would allowe him to be an excellent anatomist, but I never heard any that admired his therapeutique way. I knew several practitioners in this towne (London) that would not have given 3^d for one of his bills; and that a man could hardly tell by one of his bills what he did aime at.

'He did not care for chymistrey, and was wont to speak against them [sic Edit.] with undervalue.

'His practice was not very great towards his latter end,

he declined it, unlesse to a very speciall friend,—e.g., my Lady Howland, who had a cancer in her breast, which he did cut off and seared, but at last she dyed of it.'

To return, however, to Harvey's death; after sending for his nephews, 'he made sign to Sambroke, his Apothecary, in Black-Fryars, to let him blood in the tongue, which did little or no good, and so he ended his dayes. . . . The palsie did give him an easie passeport,' added Aubrey.

D'Arcy Power summed up by saying that Harvey apparently died of a cerebral haemorrhage from vessels long injured by gout, and situated at the base or internal parts of the brain rather than in the frontal lobes.

The body was brought to London and was apparently placed in Eliab Harvey's Cockaine House, in the room which was later the office of the antiquary of Oxford renown, Elias Ashmole. Though Harvey died on 3 June, it was not until 25 June that the Fellows of the College of Physicians were requested to attend in their gowns on the following day. Eliab as Executor decided that Harvey should be buried at Hempstead, and the funeral procession left on 26 June, to be followed by a large number of the Fellows. 'Many of whom,' says D'Arcy Power, 1897, 'must afterwards have hurried back to Westminster Hall where, on the same day, with the greatest ceremony and with all the pomp of circumstance, Cromwell was a second time inaugurated after the humble petition and advice had given him the power of nominating his successors and of forming a Second House of Parliament, while it assigned to him a perpetual revenue.'

The funeral cortège must have taken a considerable time to reach Hempstead, situated as it was about fifty miles from London, where Eliab Harvey had, about two years previously, built the Harvey chapel on the north side of the church and communicating with the chancel. In the fashion of the family, simple wrapping of the body in lead had been carried out, and Harvey's body was placed between those of his nieces, Sarah and Elizabeth, with an indication in large letters on his breast that it was of Doctor William Harvey deceased the 3 of June 1657 aged 79 years.

In 1847 his place of sepulture was visited by Sir Benjamin Ward Richardson, and some repairs were made thereafter in the vault, but it took a second visit ten years later before much further was done. Very probably Harvey's remains would have been placed in what Sir Benjamin called 'their one fit and final resting place, namely, Westminster Abbey', but the then Dean, Dr Stanley, who was apparently sympathetic to the proposal, unfortunately died before it could be carried into action, and then, on 28 January 1882, the Hempstead church tower fell towards the south-west into the churchyard. A committee of the College sat, and on its recommendation it was decided to leave Harvey's remains in the church at Hempstead, but to remove them to a marble sarcophagus to be placed, on a floor suitably strengthened, in the chapel above the vault.

On St Luke's Day, 1883, the leaden case containing the remains was reverently carried from the vault by eight Fellows of the College, and was at once deposited in the sarcophagus in the presence of the President, Office Bearers, and many Fellows.

Then, on 7 July 1933, in connection with the rebuilding of the tower of Hempstead Church, near Saffron Walden, as a memorial to William Harvey, the foundation stone was laid by Lord Dawson of Penn, President of the Royal College and of the British Medical Association. The Harveian Society of London continues a close association with the Church.

REFERENCES

Adelmann, H. B. (1942). 'The embryological treatises of Hier-onymus Fabricius of Aquapendente. The formation of the egg and of the chick [*De formatione ovi et pulli*]. The formed foetus [*De formato foetu*].' A facsimile edition, with an introduction, a translation, and a commentary. Ithaca, New York: Cornell University Press.

Alberti, S. (1585). 'De valvulis membraneis quorundam vaso-rum', etc. In his: *Tres orationes*, etc.

Allison, J. J. (1839). 'Experiments proving the existence of a venous pulse independent of the heart and nervous system, with remarks on contractility of the veins in general.' *Amer. J. med. Sci.*, *23*, 306–23.

Andrew, J. (1890). 'The Harveian Oration.' London, 1891: Adlard & Son.

Anon. (1957). New translation of 'De motu cordis'. *Brit. med. J.*, i, 1292–93.

Anon. (1959). 'Abdominal decompression in labour.' Leader. *Lancet*, 14, 41–42.

Aselli, G. (1627). *De lactibus sive lacteis venis, quarto vasorum meseraicorum genere, novo invento* . . . Mediolani: apud J. B. Bidellum.

Assenfeldt, N. van (1650). 'A premature "threnody" on the death of Harvey', ed. by W. W. Francis's Hisc. med., *Ch.*, 254–55.

Aubrey, J. (1813). *Memories of lives*, ed. O. L. Dick, London: Secker & Warburg.

Baier, J. J. (1728). *Biographiae professorum medicinae qui in academia Altorfina unquam vixerunt.* Nuremburg.

Barclay, J. (1582–1621). *Argenis* (a political romance).

Barlow, T. (1957). 'Harvey, the man and the physician.' The Harveian Oration delivered before the Royal College of

Physicians of London on St Luke's Day, 1916, reprinted in *Brit. med. J.*, i, 1264–71.

Bayon, H. P. (1938–39). 'William Harvey, physician and biologist: his precursors, opponents, and successors. Parts I-V.' *Ann. Sci.*, *3*, 59–118, 435–56, *4*, 66–106, 329–89.

Bayon, H. P. (1939). 'Allusions to a "circulation" of the blood in M.S.S. anterior to *De motu cordis 1628.*' *Proc. R. Soc. Med.*, *32*, 707–18.

Bayon, H. P. (1951). 'The lifework of William Harvey and modern medical progress.' *Proc. R. Soc. Med.*, *44*, 213–18. *Sect. Hist. Med.*, 13–18.

Belloc, H. (1936). *Charles the First: King of England.* 3rd Edn. London: London, Toronto, Melbourne and Sydney: Cassell and Company Ltd.

Bernard, C. (1855–56). *Leçons de physiologie expérimentale appliquée à la médicine.* Paris: J. B. Baillière.

Bishop, W. J., and Poynter, F. N. L. (1947). 'The Harveian Orations, 1656–1947, A study in tradition.' *Brit. med. J.*, ii, 622–23.

Boenheim, F. (1957). 'From Huang-Ti to Harvey.' *J. Hist. Med.*, *12*, 181–88.

Böving, B. G. (1959). 'The biology of trophoblast.' *Ann. N.Y. Acad. Sci.*, *80*, 21–43.

Boyle, R. (1744). *The works of the Honourable Robert Boyle* in 5 volumes, ed. T. Birch. London: Millar.

Bradford, J. R. (1933). 'The Harvey Memorial Tower.' *Brit. med. J.*, ii, 28–29.

Brain, W. R. (1959). 'William Harvey, Neurologist.' *Brit. med. J.*, ii, 899–905.

Brunton, T. L. (1894). *Modern developments of Harvey's work.* London: Macmillan and Co.

Brunton, T. L., and Fayrer, J. (1876). 'Notes on independent pulsation of the pulmonary veins and vena cava.' *Proc. roy. Soc.*, *25*, 174–76.

Buzzard, E. F. (1941). 'Reconstruction in the practice of medicine.' *Lancet*, 1942, i, 343–47.

Caesalpinus, A. The Canonici MSS. notes of Caesalpino's 1590 lectures at Pisa. Oxford: The Bodleian Library.

Capparoni, P. (1932). *La storia della scoperta della circolazione del sangue*. Siena: Stab. tip. S. Bernardino.

Caux, D. de (1674). *Varia philosophica et medica*.

Cawadias, A. P. (1958). 'Harvey in Padua,' 47–53 in *Circulation*, ed. J. McMichael. Oxford: Blackwell Scientific Publications.

Chadwick, J., and Mann, W. N. (1946). '*The medical works of Hippocrates*. A new translation.' Oxford: Blackwell Scientific Publications.

Champy, C., and Louvel, J. (1938). 'La contraction de la veine cave supérieure.' *Bull. acad. med.*, *119*, 718–20.

Charles, J. (1955). 'The contrivance of collegiation.' *Lancet*, ii, 987–93.

Chauvois, L. (1923). *Les dessanglés du ventre, etc*. Paris: Maloine.

Chauvois, L. (1923). *Un danger social: la constipation*. Paris: Maloine.

Chauvois, L. (1926). *La machine humaine enseignée par la machine automobile*. Paris: Gaston Doin & Cie.

Chauvois, L. (1952). *Place aux veines, ou rôle initial du secteur veineux dans le circuit sanguin*. Paris: Amédie Legrand & Cie.

Chauvois, L. (1957). 'On William Harvey at Padua and the way in which he was stimulated to reinvestigate the problem of heart and blood movements and on the credit he merits for the discovery.' *J. Hist. Med.*, *12*, 175–80.

Chauvois, L. (1957). 'De Motu Cordis.' *Discovery*, September, 404.

Chauvois, L. (1958). 'Harvey and French medicine,' 54–58 in *Circulation*, ed. J. McMichael. Oxford: Blackwell Scientific Publications.

Choulant, L. (1945). 'History and bibliography of anatomic illustration.' New York: Schuman's.

Cohen, H. (1950). 'Harvey and the scientific method.' *Brit. med. J.*, ii, 1405–10.

Cohen, Lord, of Birkenhead (1957). 'The germ of an idea or What put Harvey on the scent.' *J. Hist. Med.*, *12*, 102–05.

Cohn, A. E. (1928). 'The development of the Harveian circulation.' *Ann. med. Hist.*, *1*, 16–36.

Cole, F. J. (1955). 'Bell's law.' *Notes roy. Soc. Lond.*, *11*, 222–27.

Cole, F. J. (1957). 'Harvey's animals.' *J. Hist. Med.*, *12*, 106–13.

Cole, F. J. (1957). 'William Harvey (1578–1657).' *Nature*, *179*, 103–05.

Combebale, P. (1924). 'Sur la nature et l'origine des courants sanguins observés dans le système veineux après l'arrêt du coeur.' *C.R. Soc. Biol. Paris*, *90*, 1417–18.

Conring, H. (1643). *De sanguinis generatione et motu naturali; opus novum*. Helmstadt.

Cope, Z. (1959). 'William Harvey and his brothers.' *Brit. med. J.*, ii, 1250–51.

Crowther, J. G. (1960). *Francis Bacon*. London: The Cresset Press.

Curtis, J. G. (1915). *Harvey's views on the use of the circulation of the blood*. New York: Columbia University Press.

Dale, H. (1935). *Some epochs in medical research*. London: H. K. Lewis & Co., Ltd.

Dalton, J. C. (1884). *Doctrines of the circulation. A history of physiological opinion and discovery, in regard to the circulation of the blood*. Philadelphia: Henry C. Lea's Son & Co.

Davidson, M. (1953). *Medicine in Oxford. A historical romance*. Oxford: Basil Blackwell.

Dodds, C. (1958). 'Harvey, scientist and physician—a contrast.' 27–30 in *Circulation*, ed. J. McMichael. Oxford: Blackwell Scientific Publications.

Eales, N. B. (1959). 'Francis Joseph Cole, 1872–1959.' *J. Hist. Med.*, *14*, 267–72.

Edwards, E. A. (1958). 'The anatomy of collateral circulation.' *Surg. Gyn. Obstet.*, *107*, 183–94.

Elliotson, J. (1846). 'The Harveian Oration, delivered before the

Royal College of Physicians, London, June 27th, 1846, *etc.*' London: Bailliere.

Eloy (1778). *Dictionnaire historique de la médecine ancienne et moderne* . . . A Mons: chez H. Horjois.

Ent, G. (1641). *Apologia pro circulatione sanguinis, qua respondetur Aemilio Parisano*. Londini, excudebat Rob. Young.

Favaro, G. (1921). *L'insegnamento anatomico di Girolamo Fabrici d'Acquapendente*. Venezia: Premiate officine grafiche Carlo Ferrari.

Ferrario, E. V., Poynter, F. N. L., and Franklin, K. J., (1960). 'William Harvey's debate with Caspar Hofmann on the circulation of the blood. New documentary evidence.' *J. Hist. Med.*, *15*, 7–21.

Finch, J. S. (1950). *Sir Thomas Browne. A doctor's life of science and faith*. New York: Henry Schuman.

Fleisch, A. (1935). 'Physiologische Mechanismen der Regulierung des Blutkreislaufes.' *Schweiz. med. Wschr.*, *16*, 109–13.

Forrester, J. M. (1954). 'An experiment of Galen's repeated.' *Proc. R. Soc. Med.* *47*, 241–44.

Foster, J. (1891). *Alumni Oxonienses 1 The members of the University of Oxford 1500–1714: their parentage, birthplace, and year of birth, with a record of their degrees*. Oxford and London: James Parker & Co.

Francis, W. W. (1957). 'A premature threnody "On the death of Harvey", by N. van Assenfeldt,' ed. W. W. Francis. *J. Hist. Med.*, *12*, 254–55.

Franklin, K. J. (1928). 'Valves in veins: an historical survey.' *Proc. R. Soc. Med.*, *21*, Sect. Hist. Med., 1–33.

Franklin, K. J. (1932). Facsimile edition, with introduction and translation, of R. Lower's *Tractatus De Corde*, etc., London, 1669. (Gunther's *Early Science in Oxford*, *9*). Oxford: printed for the subscribers.

Franklin, K. J. (1933). *A short history of physiology*. London: John Bale, Sons, & Danielsson, Ltd.

Franklin, K. J. (1933). Facsimile edition, with introduction and translation, of *De venarum ostiolis*, 1603, of Hieronymus Fabricius of Aquapendente. Springfield, Ill., and Baltimore, Md.: Charles C. Thomas.

Franklin, K. J. (1937) *A monograph on veins*. Springfield, Ill., and Baltimore, Md.: Charles C. Thomas.

Franklin, K. J. (1941). 'A survey of the growth of knowledge about certain parts of the foetal cardio-vascular apparatus, and about the foetal circulation, in man and some other mammals. Part I: Galen to Harvey.' *Ann. Sci.*, *5*, 57–89.

Franklin, K. J. (1941). 'Ductus venosus [Arantii] and ductus arteriosus [Botalli].' *Bull. Hist. Med.*, *9*, 580–84.

Franklin, K. J. (1948). *Cardiovascular studies*. Oxford: Blackwell Scientific Publications.

Franklin, K. J. (1949). *A short history of physiology*. 2nd Edn. London: Staples Press, Ltd. New York: Staples Press Inc.

Franklin, K. J. (1952). 'The history of circulatory research, leading to a wider view of the circulation.' *Trans. Coll. Phys. Philad.*, 4 *s.*, *20*, 23–33.

Franklin, K. J. (1957). *William Harvey's Exercitatio anatomica de motu cordis et sanguinis in animalibus, 1628*, newly done into English by Kenneth J. Franklin. Oxford: published for the Royal College of Physicians of London by Blackwell Scientific Publications.

Franklin, K. J., and du Boulay, G. (1957). 'Variations on a theme of Harvey.' *St. Bart's Hosp. J.*, *61*, 171–73.

Franklin, K. J. (1958). 'A translation of *De circulatione sanguinis*.' *St. Bart's Hosp. J.*, *62*, 50–54.

Franklin, K. J. (1958). 'Introduction,' 3–10, to *Circulation*, ed. J. McMichael. Oxford: Blackwell Scientific Publications.

Franklin, K. J. (1960). 'Francis Joseph Cole, 1872–1959.' *Obit. Not. roy. Soc.*, *5*, 37–47.

Fraser-Harris, D. F. (1934). 'William Harvey's knowledge of literature: classical, mediaeval, renaissance and contemporary.' *Med. Press*, *189*, 164–69; 184–87, and *Proc. R. Soc. Med.*, *27*, 1095–99.

Fulton, J. F. (1958). 'Completing Harvey's work: discovery of the capillaries—Malpighi, Leeuwenhoek, and Hales.' 20–26 in *Circulation*, ed. J. McMichael, Oxford: Blackwell Scientific Publications.

Garrod, A. E. (1923). *Inborn errors of metabolism*, 2nd Edn. London: Henry Frowde *and* Hodder & Stoughton.

Garrod, A. E. (1924). *The debt of science to medicine.* Oxford: At the Clarendon Press.

Gollwitzer-Meier, K. (1931). 'Venensystem und Kreislaufregulation.' *Klin. Wschr.*, *10*, 817–21.

Goltz, F. (1864). 'Ueber den Tonus der Gefässe und seine Bedeutung für die Blutbewegung.' *Virchows Arch.*, *29*, 394–432.

Gotfredsen, E. (1952). 'The reception of Harvey's doctrine in Denmark.' *Acta med. scand.*, suppl. *266*, 75–86.

Graham, G. (1953). 'The value of physiology in medicine.' Harveian Oration, 1953. *Brit. med. J.*, 1954, ii, 225–33.

Graves, R. E. (1888). 'Article on Wm Dobson (1610–46).' D.N.B. *15*, 137–38. London: Smith, Elder, & Co.

Gray, A. (1951). 'Dermatology from the time of Harvey.' *Lancet*, ii, 795–802.

Gulland, G. L. (1930). 'The circulating fluid.' The Harveian Oration delivered 30 May 1930. *Edinb. med. J.*, N.S. *37*, 569–81.

Gunn, J. A., and Chavasse, F. B. (1913). 'The action of adrenin on veins.' (Preliminary communication). *Proc. Roy. Soc.*, B, *86*, 192–97.

Guthrie, D. (1957). 'The Harveian tradition in Scotland.' *J. Hist. Med.*, *12*, 120–25.

Haddad, S. I., and Khairallah, A. A. (1936). 'A forgotten chapter in the circulation of the blood.' *Amn. Surg.*, *164*, 1–8.

Hamilton, W. J., Harrison, R. J., and Young, B. A. (1960). 'Aspects of placentation in certain Cervidae.' *J. Anat., Lond.*, *94*, 1–33.

Harrison, R. J., and Hyett, A. R. (1954). 'The development and growth of the placentomes in the fallow deer (*Dama Dama L*).' *J. Anat., Lond.*, *88*, 338–55.

Hamusco, J. V. de (1556). *De la composicion del cuerpo humano.* Rome.

Hare, T. (1958). 'Harvey's boyhood.' 32–34 in *Circulation*, ed. J. McMichael. Oxford: Blackwell Scientific Publications.

Harvey, W. (1653). *Anatomical exercitations, concerning the generation of living creatures: to which are added particular discourses, of births, and of conceptions, &c.* London: printed by James Young, for Octavian Pulleyn.

Harvey, W. (1766). *Opera omnia: a Collegio Medicorum Londinensi edita.*

Harvey, W. (1847). *The works of . . . translated from the Latin with a life of the author by Robert Willis, M.D. . . .* London: Printed for the Sydenham Society.

Harvey, W. (1886). *Praelectiones anatomiæ universalis.* Ed. for the Royal College of Physicians of London. London: J. & A. Churchill.

Harvey, W. (1958). *Circulation of the blood: Two anatomical essays by William Harvey, together with nine letters written by him, the whole translated from the Latin and slightly annotated by Kenneth J. Franklin.* Oxford: Blackwell Scientific Publications.

Henderson, Y., Oughterson, A. W., Greenberg, L. A., and Searle, C. P. (1934). 'The third major mechanical factor in the circulation of the blood.' *Science*, *79*, 508–10.

Herringham, W. (1928). 'William Harvey at St Bartholomew's.' *St. Bart's Hosp. J.*, *35*, 133–5.

Herringham, W. (1929). *Circumstances in the life and times of William Harvey.* Oxford: At the Clarendon Press.

Herringham, W. (1932). 'The life and times of Dr. William Harvey.' *Ann. med. Hist.*, n.s. *4*, 109–25, 249–72, 347–63, 491–502, 575–89.

Hervey, M. F. S. (1921). *The Life, correspondence and collections of Thomas Howard, Earl of Arundel.* Cambridge: At the University Press.

Highmore, N. (1651). *Corporis humani disquisitio anatomica.* Hagae-Comitis, Ex officina Samuelis Broun Bibliopolae Anglici.

Hind, A. M. (1922). *Wenceslaus Hollar and his views of London and Windsor in the seventeenth century*. London: John Lane the Bodley Head Limited.

Hobbes, T. (1680). *Behemoth. The history of the civil wars of England, from the year 1640 to 1660*. Purged from the errours of former Ed^{ns}. Printed in the year 1680. in the English works of Thomas Hobbes of Malmesbury, now first collected and edited by Sir William Molesworth, 6. London: John Brown.

Hofmann, C. (1652). *Digressio ad circulationem sanguinis in Anglia natam*. Parisiis: apud Casp. Meturas.

Hooker, D. R. (1920). 'The functional activities of the capillaries and venules.' *Amer. J. Physiol.*, 54, 30–54.

Hume, W. E. (1943). *The physician in war—in Harvey's time and after*. Newcastle-upon-Tyne: Andrew Reid & Company Limited.

Hunter, R. A., and Macalpine, I. (1956). 'William Harvey—two medical anecdotes. The one related by Sir Kenelm Digby, the other by the Honourable Robert Boyle.' *St. Bart's Hosp. J.*, 60, 200–6.

Hunter, R. A., and Macalpine, I. (1957). 'Notes and events. A note on William Harvey's *Nan Gunter* (1616).' *J. Hist. Med.*, 12, 512–15.

Hunter, R. A., and Macalpine, I. (1958). 'William Harvey and Robert Boyle.' *Notes roy. Soc. Lond.*, 13, 115–27.

Hunter, Richard A., and Macalpine, Ida. (1960). Harvey's 'Boy abowt Holborn Bridg'. In Notes and Events. *J. Hist. Med.*, 15, 295–96.

Hutchison, R. (1931). 'Harvey: the man, his method, and his message for us today.' *Brit. med. J.*, ii, 733–39.

Huxley, S. (1959). *Endymion Porter. The life of a Courtier 1587–1649*. London: Chatto & Windus.

Ibn an-Nafis. *See* Meyerhof, M. (1935).

Innes-Smith, R. (1959). 'The discovery of the King's body.' *The royal Martyr memorial*, 15–17.

Jameson, W. (1942). 'War and the advancement of social medicine.' *Lancet*, ii, 475–80.

Janker, R. (1933). 'Die Rontgenkinematographie, ein Forschungs – und lehrimittel.' *Dtsch. Z. Chir.*, *240*, 52–61.

Johnson, G. (1882). 'The Harveian Oration.' London: Smith, Elder & Co.

Keele, H. D. (1957). 'William Harvey: The Man and the College of Physicians.' *Med. Hist.*, *1*, 265–78.

Keynes, G. (1949). *The personality of William Harvey*. Cambridge: At the University Press.

Keynes, G. (1949). *The portraiture of William Harvey*. London: The Royal College of Surgeons of England.

Keynes, G. (1950). 'The portraits of William Harvey.' *Brit. med. J.*, ii, 43. Cf. Singer, C. *ibid.*, i, 1259–60.

Keynes, G. (1953). *A bibliography of the writings of Dr. William Harvey 1578–1657*, 2nd Edn., revised. Cambridge: At the University Press.

Keynes, G. (1958). 'Introduction' to Harvey's Life, 31 in *Circulation*, ed. J. McMichael. Oxford: Blackwell Scientific Publications.

Keynes, G. (1958). 'Harvey through John Aubrey's eyes.' *Lancet*, ii, 859–64.

Kilgour, F. G. (1954). 'William Harvey's use of the quantitative method.' *Yale J. Biol. Med.*, *26*, 410–21.

Kilgour, F. G. (1957). 'Harvey's use of Galen's findings in his discovery of the circulation of the blood.' *J. Hist. Med.*, *12*, 232–34.

Knoll, P. (1897). 'Ueber den Einfluss des Herzvagus auf die Zusammenziehungen der Vena Cava superior beim Säugethier.' *Pflüg. Arch. ges. Physiol.*, *68*, 339–47.

Krumbhaar, E. B. (1957). 'Thoughts on bibliographies and Harvey's writings.' *J. Hist. Med.*, *12*, 235–40.

Lakin, C. E. (1947). *Our founders and benefactors*. London: Headley Brothers.

Leibowitz, J. O. (1957). 'Early accounts of the valves in the veins.' *J. Hist. Med.*, *12*, 189–96.

Lewis, T. (1933). 'Clinical science.' *Brit. med. J.*, ii, 717–22.

Lindroth, S. (1957). 'Harvey, Descartes, and young Olaus Rudbeck.' *J. Hist. Med.*, *12*, 209–19.

Lint, J. G. de (1926). *Atlas of the History of Medicine. I. Anatomy*, 54–61. London: H. K. Lewis & Co., Ltd.

Louvel, J., and Laubry, J. J. (1950). 'Les veines,' in *Les petits précis*. Paris: Librairie Maloine.

Lower, R. (1669). *Tractatus de corde item de motu & colore sanguinis et chyli in eum transitu*. Facsimile edition, with introduction and translation by K. J. Franklin. R. T. Gunther's Early Science in Oxford, *9*. Oxford: Printed for the subscribers. Original was London: printed by Jo. Redmayne for James Allestry.

MacNalty, A. S. (1957). 'William Harvey: his influence on public health.' The Harveian Lecture to the Royal Soc. Health. *Roy. Soc. Prom. Hlth. J.*, *77*, 324–37.

McNeil, C. (1950). 'Verities yet in their chaos.' *Brit. med. J.*, ii, 961–65.

MacWilliam, J. A. (1885). 'On the structure and rhythm of the heart in fishes, with especial reference to the heart of the eel.' *Proc. roy. Soc.*, *38*, 108–29.

Mattingly, G. (1959). *The defeat of the Spanish armada*. London: Jonathan Cape.

Meyer, A. W. (1936). *An analysis of the* De generatione animalium *of William Harvey*. Stanford, Calif.: Stanford University Press. London: Humphrey Milford, Oxford University Press.

Meyer, A. W. (1939). *The rise of embryology*. Stanford, Calif.: Stanford University Press. London: Humphrey Milford, Oxford University Press.

Meyer, A. W. (1956). *Human generation. Conclusions of Burdach, Döllinger and von Baer*. Stanford, Calif.: Stanford University Press. London: Geoffrey Cumberlege, Oxford University Press.

Meyerhof, M. (1935). 'Ibn an-Nafis (XIIIth cent.) and his theory of the lesser circulation.' *Isis*, *23*, 100–20.

Moore, N. (1901). 'The Harveian Oration.' London: John Murray.

Moran, Lord (1952). 'On credulity.' Harveian Oration for 1952. *Lancet*, 1954, i, 167–72.

Moschetti, A. (1913). *Italia artistica.* Padova.

Muirhead, Arnold (1939). Translation of *Anatomia Thomae Parri*, by William Harvey. 1635. See *Bart's Hosp. Rep. 72.*

Munk, W. (1887). 'Notae Harveianae.' *St. Bart's Hosp. Rep.*, *23*, 1–12.

Nardi, G. (1656). *Noctes geniales.* Bologna.

Newman, G. (1922). *A century of medicine at Padua.* London: British Periodicals, Ltd.

Newman, G. (1932). 'The debt of preventive medicine to Harvey and the College of Physicians.' *Brit. med. J.*, ii, 739–44; *Lancet*, ii, 877–84.

O'Malley, C. D. (1957). 'A Latin translation of Ibn Nafis (1547) related to the problem of the circulation of the blood.' *J. Hist. Med.*, *12*, 248–53.

Osler, W. (1957). 'The growth of truth, as illustrated in the discovery of the circulation of the blood,' being the Harveian Oration delivered at the Royal College of Physicians, 18 October 1906. Reprinted in *Brit. med. J.*, i, 1257–63.

Pagel, W. (1948). 'A background study to Harvey.' *Med. Bookm.*, *2*, 407–9.

Pagel, W. (1950). 'Harvey's role in the history of medicine.' *Bull. Hist. Med.*, *24*, 70–73.

Pagel, W. (1951). 'William Harvey and the purpose of circulation.' *Isis*, *42*, 22–38.

Pagel, W. (1951). 'Giordano Bruno: the philosophy of circles and the circular movement of the blood.' *J. Hist. Med.*, *6*, 116–24.

Pagel, W. (1957). 'The philosophy of circles—Cesalpino—Harvey. A penultimate assessment.' *J. Hist. Med.*, *12*, 140–57.

Paget, C. G. (1929). *By-ways in the history of Croydon.* Croydon: the Central Library, Town Hall.

Paget, C. G. (1937). *Croydon homes of the past*. Croydon: the Central Library, Town Hall.

Paget, J. (1846). *Records of Harvey: in extracts from the Journals of the Royal Hospital of St Bartholomew*. Published by permission of the President and Treasurer. With notes by James Paget. London: John Churchill.

Parkinson, J. (1945). 'Rheumatic fever and heart disease.' *Lancet*, ii, 657–63.

Parsons, L. (1950). *The influence of Harvey and his contemporaries on paediatrics*. London: Headley Brothers.

Payne, J. F. (1896). *Harvey and Galen*. London 1897: Henry Frowde, Oxford University Press.

Payne, L. M. (1956). Notes and queries. 'Harvey at Padua and after.' *J. Hist. Med.*, *11*, 342–43.

Payne, L. M. (1957). 'Sir Charles Scarburgh's Harveian Oration, 1662.' *J. Hist. Med.*, *12*, 158–64.

Payne, L. M. (1960). 'Title of the Royal College of Physicians of London.' *Brit. med. J.*, i, 123–24.

Pazzini, A. (1957). 'William Harvey, disciple of Girolamo Fabrizi d'Acquapendente and the Paduan school.' *J. Hist. Med.*, *12*, 197–201.

Pecquet, J. (1651). *'Joannis Pecqueti Diepaei experimenta nova anatomica, quibus incognitum lactenus chyli receptaculum, et ab eo per thoracem in ramos usque subclavios vasa lactea deteguntur. Equidem dissertatio anatomica de circulatione sanguinis, et chyli motu.'* Parisiis: apud Sebastianum Cremoisy.

Pollock, J. E. (1889). 'The Harveian Oration.' London: Cassell & Company, Limited.

Powell, R. D. (1914). 'Advances in knowledge regarding the circulation and attributes of the blood since Harvey's time.' *Lancet*, ii, 979–84, 1031–36.

Power, D'Arcy (1897). *William Harvey*. London: T. Fisher Unwin.

Power, D'Arcy (1922). 'Dʳ William Harvey as a man and as an

art connoisseur.' *C.R. II Congr. Internat. d'Hist. Méd.*, Evreux, 452–56.

Power, D'Arcy (1931). 'A revised chapter in the life of Dʳ. William Harvey, 1636.' In *Selected writings, 1877–1930.* Oxford: At the Clarendon Press.

Power, H. (1664). B. M. Sloan MS. 1343, written 1652, has a section, entitled, *Circulatio harveiana inventa ab authore A.D. 1614.*

Power, H. (1664). *Experimental philosophy, in three books* containing new experiments, etc. London: J. Martin & J. Allestry.

Poynter, F. N. L. (1956). 'An unnoticed contemporary English poem in praise of Harvey and its author, John Collop, M.D.' *J. Hist. Med.*, *11*, 374–83.

Poynter, F. N. L. (1957). 'Current thought on Harvey.' *Brit. med. J.*, i, 1297–99.

Poynter, F. N. L. (1957). 'William Harvey's last will and testament.' *J. Hist. Med.*, *12*, 165–66.

Prendergast, J. S. (1930). 'Galen on the vascular system.' Oxford B.Litt. thesis.

Primrose or Primerose, J. (1630). *Exercitationes, et animadversiones in librum, de motu cordis et circulatione sanguinis, adversus Guliel- mum Harveum medicum regium & anatomes in collegio Londinensi professorem.* Londini: excudebat Gulielmus Jones pro Nicolao Bourne.

Reichert, F. L. (1929). 'Marcus Aurelius Severinus (1580–1656). A contemporary of Harvey, and author of the first work on comparative anatomy.' *Calif. West. Med.*, *30*, No. 3.

Reynolds, J. R. (1884). 'The Harveian Oration.' London: J. & A. Churchill.

Riml, O. (1929). 'Über das Verhalten des Blutdruckes in der Vena cava bei plötzlichen zirkulationstillstande.' *Arch. exp. Path. Pharmak.*, *139*, 231–39.

Riolan, J., Jun. (1649). *Encheiridium anatomicum et pathologicum. In quo ex naturali constitutione partium, recessus a naturali statu demonstratur. ad usum Theatri Anatomici adornatum.* Lugcuni Batavorum, Ex officina Adriani Wyngerden.

Riviera, D. (1946). *Sul Frescos enel Instituto nacional di Cardiologia por el Doctor Ignacio Chavez miembro Fundador de el colegio nacional.*

Robertson, J. L. (1908). *A History of English literature.* Edinburgh and London: William Blackwood and Sons.

Roesler, H. (1937). *Pre-Harveian concepts of the circulation.* 6, No. 5.

Rolleston, G. (1873). 'The Harveian Oration', 729–68 in *Scientific papers and addresses,* 2, Oxford, 1884. At the Clarendon Press.

Rolleston, H. D. (1928). *Cardio-vascular diseases since Harvey's discovery.* Cambridge: At the University Press.

Rolleston, H. (1928). 'Harvey's predecessors and contemporaries.' *Ann. med. Hist.,* 10, 323–37.

Rothschuh, K. E. (1957). 'Über Kreislaufschemata und Kreislaufmodelle seic den Zeiten von William Harvey (1578–1657).' *Z. KreislForsch.,* 46, 241–49.

Roughton, F. J. W. (1958). 'Harvey at Cambridge.' 35–42 in *Circulation,* ed. J. McMichael. Oxford: Blackwell Scientific Publications.

Royal College of Physicians (1957). *William Harvey 1578–1657. An exhibition of books and manuscripts illustrating his life and work.* London: Royal College of Physicians.

Ruysch, F. (1729). *Adversaria anatomica.* Amsterdam.

Salter, G. H. (1956). *A watcher at the City-gate for thirty-eight reigns A.D. 1137–1956.* London: Hodder & Stoughton, 71–72.

Sándor, G. (1926). 'Vergleichende Untersuchungen an den Froschgefässen mit besonderer Berücksichtigung des Gehirns.' *Pflüg. Arch. ges. Physiol.,* 213, 492–510.

Sarton, G. (1920). 'The faith of a humanist.' *Isis,* 3, 3–6.

Schlegel, P. M. (1650). *De sanguinis motu commentatio, in qua praecipue in Joh. Riolani, V.C. sententiam inquiritur.* Hamburgi, Typis Jacobi Rebenlini.

Schott, A. (1956). 'Historical notes on the iconography of the heart.' *Cardiologia,* 28, 229–68.

Senac (1749). *Traité de la structure du coeur, de son action, & de ses maladies.* Paris: chez Briasson.

Sherrington, C. S. (1919). *Note on the history of the word 'tonus' as a physiological term.* Contributions to medical and biological research dedicated to Sir William Osler in honour of his seventieth birthday, 12 July 1919, by his pupils and co-workers. *1,* 261–68. New York: Paul B. Hoeber.

Singer, C. (1950). 'A newly discovered portrait of William Harvey.' *Brit. med. J.,* i, 1259–60.

Spencer, H. R. (1921). *William Harvey, Obstetric physician and gynaecologist.* London: Harrison and Sons, Ltd.

Spencer, H. R. (1929). *Medicine in the days of Shakespeare.* London: John Bale, Sons, & Danielsson, Ltd.

Spriggs, E. (1944). *The Harveian method in literature.* London: Headley Brothers.

Stewart, D. (1946). 'Harvey and the battle of Edgehill.' *Brit. med. J.,* i, 808.

Trueta, J. (1957). 'The predecessors of Harvey.' *Oxford med. Sch. Gaz.,* 2, 91–95.

Underwood, E. A. (1952). 'English medicine and the Italian renaissance.' *Rev. stor. sci. med. e nat.,* 43, 215–24.

Viets, H. R. (1957). 'Young Montgomery and his beating heart.' *New Eng. J. Med.,* 256, 702–3.

Volta, A. D. (1958). 'Harvey at Padua.' 43–46 in *Circulation,* ed. J. McMichael. Oxford: Blackwell Scientific Publications.

Wale, J. de, or Walaeus, J. (1641). *Epistola ad Casp. Bartholin de motu chyli et sanguinis.* In Casp. Bartholini, D. & Profes. Regii Institutiones anatomicae. Lugd. Batavorum; apud Franciscum Hackum.

Walshe, F. M. R. (1948). *The structure of medicine and its place among the sciences.* Edinburgh: E. & S. Livingstone Ltd.

Warren, W. (died 1640). British Museum MSS. in Birch Collection 466 folio pp.

Weil, E. (1957). 'The echo of Harvey's *De motu cordis* (1628), 1628 to 1657.' *J. Hist. Med.,* 12, 167–74.

Whitteridge, G. (1958). 'De motu locali animalium, 1627.' 59–64 in *Circulation*, ed. J. McMichael. Oxford: Blackwell Scientific Publications.

Whitteridge, G. (1959). 'William Harvey *De motu locali animalium* 1627,' ed., trans. and introduced by Dr Gweneth Whitteridge. Cambridge: At the University Press.

Wiggers, C. J. (1957). Harvey Tercentenary Lecture. 'The impact of Harvey and his work on circulation research.' *Circulation Res.*, 5, 335–48.

Wright, A. D. (1958). President's opening address. xxi–xxiii in *Circulation*, ed. J. McMichael. Oxford: Blackwell Scientific Publications.

Young, R. A. (1939). *The pulmonary circulation—before and after Harvey*. London: Headley Brothers.

INDEX